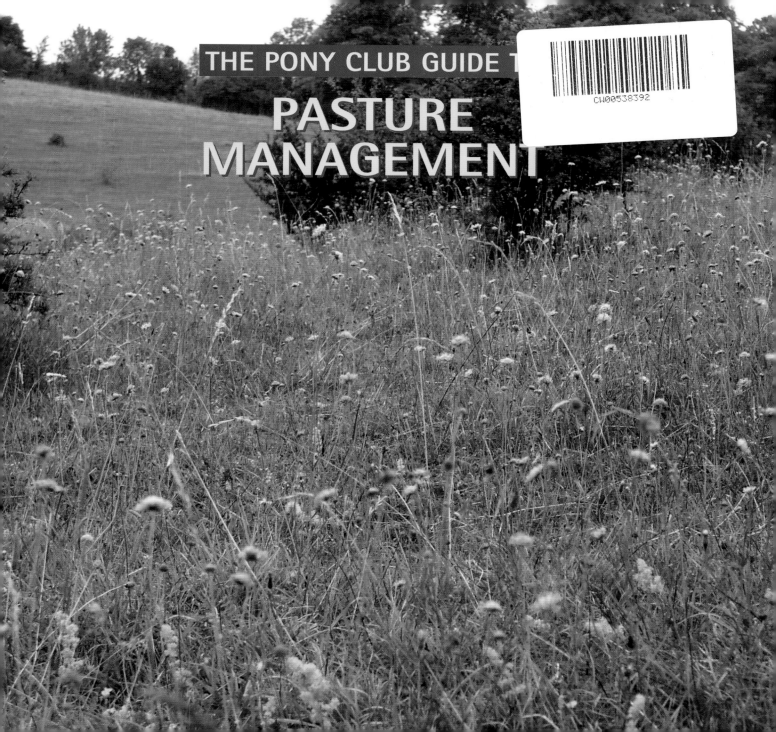

THE PONY CLUB GUIDE T

PASTURE
MANAGEMENT

(Above) A hayfield containing a variety of grasses and flowers, ideal for horses, either as hay or for aftermath grazing.

(Previous page) Chalk grassland contains many wildflowers, and its diversity, low fertility, and free-draining qualities suit horses well.

(Cover) Ponies at Shipton Connemara Stud, surrounded by diverse vegetation (including trees and bushes) and relaxed in each other's company. Buttercups and daisies are two plants which withstand hard grazing and heavy wear, and although a range of grasses and flowers is desirable, buttercups are best avoided. However, although they are toxic and cause skin allergies in some horses, they are rarely eaten unless food is short.

THE PONY CLUB GUIDE TO

PASTURE MANAGEMENT

ELIZABETH O'BEIRNE-RANELAGH

First published in 2010 by

The Pony Club
Stoneleigh Park
Kenilworth
Warwickshire
CV8 2RW

Produced for the Pony Club by
Paul Harding / Compass Books

Publishing consultant Barbara Cooper

Designed by Nancy Lawrence

Printed in China

ISBN 978-0-9548863-8-7

British Library Cataloguing in Publication Data
available on request.

Text © 2010 Elizabeth O'Beirne-Ranelagh

Cover photograph: Bob Langrish

CONTENTS

ACKNOWLEDGEMENTS

Sandy Watney brought her considerable experience to my first draft. Her many detailed comments greatly improved the original text. In addition she made copious suggestions for illustrations, many of which I have followed. Jonathan Griffiths, Katrina Brown and Frances Clayton all assiduously read the typescript, pointing out errors and raising practical points; Katrina and Frances helped me greatly, providing insights, information and photographs for this book.

I am extremely grateful to Richard Greenwood MRCVS for reading Chapter 3 despite his busy schedule, and to Clare Macleod MSc Rnutr for her valuable suggestions for Chapter 1. She also helped me with some general technical questions, as did Alexandra Amick.

My interpretation of the comments and advice that I received – and any mistakes I may have made – are of course my own.

Listed here is everyone who supplied me with illustrations, sometimes taking photographs specifically for me. Natural England provided generous access to their invaluable picture library.

Tim Austin took time on a cold and snowy day to help me photograph his farm machinery.

I am most fortunate to be working once again with Maggie Raynor, whose skill and versatility in drawing is boundless, and with the Sydney-based graphic artist Peter Will, who generously responded to my countless demands for pictures across continents and time zones. The enthusiasm of Nancy Lawrence, Barbara Cooper and Nikki Herbert for this book was a constant source of encouragement.

Elizabeth O'Beirne-Ranelagh
Grantchester 2009

PICTURE CREDITS (*Figure Numbers*)

Tony Atkin (copyright, and licensed for re-use under the Creative Commons Licence) – 37 (top)
Val Burdge – 52
Cambridgeshire County Council – 11
Jim Champion (copyright, and licensed for re-use under the Creative Commons Licence) – 37 (bottom)
Frances Clayton – 9, 79, 83, 106, 108, 109 (background), 112
Cotswold Grass Seeds – 76 (right)
Florida Musuem of Natural History – 3 (photographs)
French Ministry of Culture and Communication, Regional Direction for Cultural Affairs, Rhône-Alpes Region, Regional Department of Archaeology – 1
Rebecca Inman – 45 (top), 85, 87 (left), 89
Nancy Lawrence – 10, 71
Bob Langrish – 103
Jane van Lennep - 113
Rosie Mogford – 44
Natural England Picture Library – 2, 48, 100 (right), Paul Glendell; 46 (below), 55, 58 (below left, top and below right), 62, 66, 94 (left and centre), 97 (right), 99 (left), Peter Wakely; 58 (centre), Mike Henchman; 86 (left), 95 (right), Peter Roworth; 7, 75
Christa Perry – 111
Maggie Raynor – 3 (insets), 4, 5, 13, 14, 16-31, 33, 35, 36, 49, 57, 67, 68, 74, 84, 86 (right), 87 (right), 88 (right), 92, 94 (right), 95, 96, 97 (left), 98 (right), 99 (right), 100 (left), 107
Simple Systems Ltd – 76 (left)
Camilla Swire – 77
Roger Wardle – 80 (inset), 110
Tim Warren – 4
Peter Will – 3, 38, 40, 41, 61, 69, 72, 101, 102, 105, 109

CHAPTER 1

THE CLOSE RELATIONSHIP BETWEEN PONIES AND GRASS

All horses and ponies today, whatever their type or breed, are the same species, formally known as *Equus caballus*. They are all domesticated, even those which appear to run wild like the mustangs of the American prairies or the brumbies of Australia, which are known as *feral* or (like British native ponies) *semi-feral*. The only horse remaining true to the wild type is known as Przewalski's horse, which exhibits the colouring and stand-up mane of *Equus caballus's* wild ancestors, but even this horse is now only found in captivity – in zoos or wildlife reserves.

Wild horses roamed the open grassy plains of Europe, Asia and North and South America for thousands of years before and during the last Ice Age (fig. 1), but by the time that ended 10,000 years ago they had become extinct in the Americas. The Eurasian horses which survived were directly related to our modern horses and ponies, and they were only domesticated between 5000 and 6000 years ago. This is remarkably recent: other animals have been domesticated much longer (dogs – more than 12,000 years; sheep and goats – 10,000 years; cattle – 8,000 to 10,000 years).

Whereas 5000 years may seem like a very long time, to appreciate how 'recent' this is it can be compared with what was going on in human history. Domesticated plants (arable agriculture) appeared about 9500 years ago, and the first cities were even older than that. Writing (using pictograms) dates from about 5500 years ago, at the same time that farming became established in Britain. The building of the pyramids in Egypt started 4500 years ago.

As horses became domesticated, so their wild cousins began to disappear. Their natural ranges became smaller as grasslands gave way to forests in the warmer climate after the Ice Age, and their numbers dropped as man hunted them for meat. By the beginning of the twentieth century the only wild horse which remained, apart from Przewalski's horse, was the Tarpan, and this died out shortly afterwards. The Exmoor pony (fig. 2) is meant to be the closest living relative to the original British wild horse. Other members of the *Equus* family, the zebra and wild ass, still exist in the wild, but the donkey is also fully domesticated.

Understanding how recently the horse was taken from its wild state, where it relied entirely on grasslands to support it, helps us to understand why pasture is so important for horses and ponies. Evolution takes *millions* of years, not thousands, and the horse's digestive system is still adapted to grazing vegetation.

Going back in evolutionary time, we see just how strong the relationship between horses and grass is. The first *Equus* ancestor dates to 55 million years ago: to the same time that the first grass plants occurred on earth. However, the first horses were small browsing animals – smaller even than miniature ponies today – living on leaves and twigs in the forests which then covered much of the earth's surface. As world climate and vegetation changed and grasslands increased at the expense of forests, so horses gradually evolved to become grazers. Their success in spreading around the world was intimately connected to the success of grasslands, and when the grassland range began to shrink so too did the range of wild horses.

EVOLUTION AND DOMESTICATION

The adaptations required to evolve from an animal browsing the forests to an animal grazing grassland are what makes the horse we know today – and also what makes it useful to us (fig. 3). First, and most obviously, horses needed to be able to live on grass. Unlike leaves, grass is full of

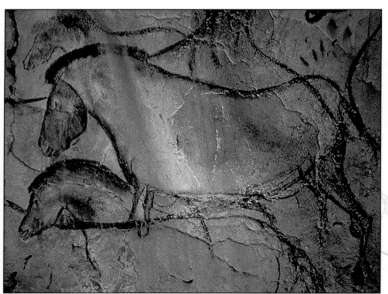

Fig. 1. Wild horses of the Ice Age depicted in cave paintings from 32,000 years ago in the south of France. Note the stand-up mane of the true wild horse.

Fig. 2. Exmoor ponies in their natural surroundings. Apart from their manes, their resemblance to their wild ancestors in the cave paintings is remarkable.

silica, which means it is highly abrasive, and a lot of chewing is required before it releases its nutrients. The horse's teeth need to be long and to grow continuously, otherwise they would wear out during a lifetime of grazing. The front teeth are used to grasp and cut off vegetation, sometimes very close to the ground. The back teeth must grind the food to a pulp before it is swallowed. The shape of the horse's head is evolved partly to accommodate these teeth, and partly to help the horse escape from enemies by allowing efficient breathing through the long nasal passages.

In order to survive in huge open spaces instead of forest, horses needed to be able to detect and escape from predators very rapidly. A horse can see to either side, both while it is grazing and when its head is raised – although to see directly behind or in front it must raise and turn its head slightly to one side. Its

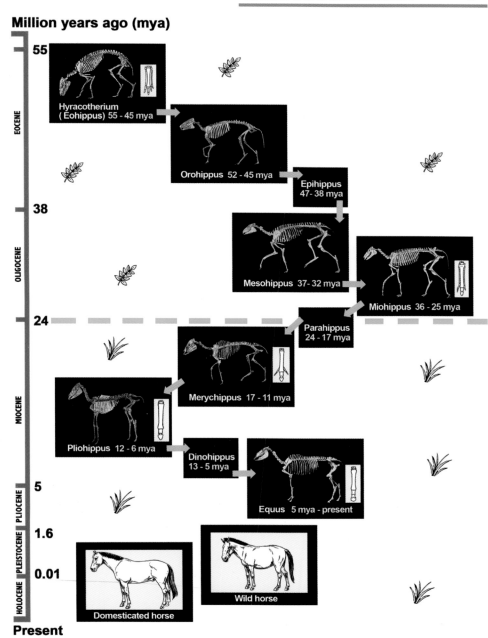

Fig. 3. The horse's evolution from the small browsing animal of the forest 55 million years ago to the horse we know today. Changes to its teeth, skeletal structure and feet gradually gave it the attributes which make it useful to mankind.

ears can swivel to catch sound from all directions. Its skeletal frame has developed with long legs to help it run faster than predators; and to compensate for long legs it has a long neck which enables it to reach the ground and graze.

The horse's digestive system also evolved to cope with a grass diet and to enable rapid escape. Many grassland plants are high in fibre and low in protein, and the horse must extract the maximum nutrition from this combination. In order to be constantly alert and able to run from predators, the horse must have an efficient digestive system, so it has only one small stomach compartment and does not need to spend time digesting or chewing cud, as cattle and sheep do with their ruminant stomachs (characteristically divided into four compartments – fig. 4). This fact, together with speed, strength and tractability (particularly receptiveness to being trained), is what made horses attractive to human beings for domestication.

Through domestication humans began to have control over horses' external characteristics, breeding them selectively for particular purposes. Different *types* had already evolved to cope with different wild habitats – for example, hot desert, wet marsh and mountains – and humans refined these types further to produce cobs, ponies, carthorses and racehorses adapted to specific uses. Later, humans developed different *breeds* of horse by registering parentage and laying down rules for conformation and ability, and so produced Thoroughbreds, Shires and Dales, for example. All horses and ponies of whatever breed or type are still evolved to be at grass – domestication and breeding have not made any basic changes to evolution. The more 'primitive' the breed the

more clearly we can see this relationship: ponies bred to live on mountain or moorland may become obese and prone to laminitis when kept on managed pasture, whereas Thoroughbreds are not hardy and may suffer if left out in wet and windy weather.

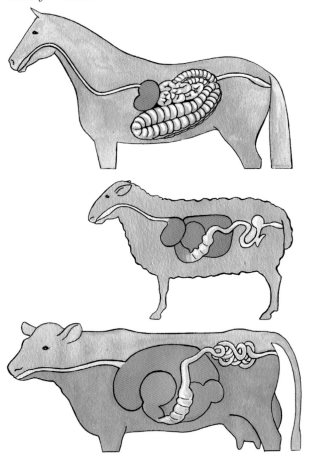

Fig. 4 The digestive systems of horses, sheep and cattle: the small stomach (dark pink) of the horse and the large 'hind gut' (pale pink) compared with the large, compartmentalised stomach of sheep and cattle.

Ponies are generally defined as 14.2 hands (147 cm) or under, but this is not a hard and fast rule. Horses used in polo are always referred to as 'ponies', but ponies from Iceland are always called 'horses'. Arabs and Welsh Cobs are often the same size as – even if they are not called – ponies. So we should not become caught up with a word, and in this book 'horse' will apply to all members of the family, whatever their breeding, characteristics and physiology. 'Pony' will only be used when it is important to distinguish the smaller types.

DIGESTIVE SYSTEM AND NUTRITIONAL NEEDS

To examine the relationship between horses and grass we can look more closely at their digestive system. Because horses have such small stomachs for their size, they need to eat small amounts almost constantly to obtain enough nutrition. Because they are adapted to eating coarse, fibrous food with low nutritive value they must eat a very large amount to extract the energy they need. All animals must get energy from their food – energy in the sense of fuel – just to stay alive. The more work an animal does the more energy it needs, so a racehorse will need more energy from its food than a retired pony. Conversely, if a horse is too energetic or too fat – unused 'fuel' is stored as fat – it may be getting more energy from its food than it needs for the amount of work it is doing.

For the horse to get enough energy from grazing, its food must pass through the system quite quickly. After using its upper lip and front teeth to select and bite off vegetation (which is sometimes then discarded from the mouth if the horse finds it unsuitable – a deliberate act of sorting, and not to be confused with 'quidding'), the horse must chew for long enough to break down the food and produce sufficient saliva to aid in swallowing and digestion. The food enters the stomach, where it goes rapidly through the first stage of digestion, passing into the small intestine after only a few hours. During the hour or so which the food spends in the small intestine, enzymes help to digest most of the protein and starch before the food passes into the large intestine, or hind gut. The hind gut is made up of the caecum, the large colon, the small colon and the rectum, and is where much of the water present in the food (water may form 65 to 85% of a grass diet) is absorbed, and micro-organisms break down the fibrous plant remains into a form which the horse can digest. The whole process can take from 48 to 72 hours, and for much the greater part of that time it is the large intestine which is doing the work (fig. 5).

Horses at grass, whether living in semi-wild conditions or at pasture, generally eat for about 16 hours a day. The amount of food they can take in depends on the amount in each bite, the number of bites, and the time spent grazing. If there is not much acceptable vegetation available, or if it is very short, then the horse will take in less than if there is plenty of good vegetation, for they only vary their grazing time by a few hours. Horses surrounded by plenty of vegetation will simply eat more than those who have to search for their food. But going without food for as little as four hours can cause problems for the horse's

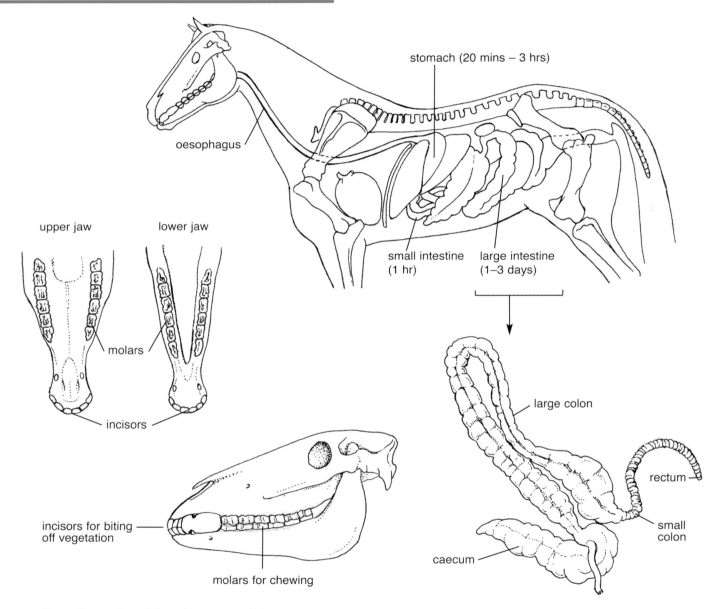

Fig. 5. The teeth and digestive system of the horse. The majority of digestive work takes place in the large intestine, or hind gut. The time the food takes to pass through each digestive stage is shown.

digestive system, as can sudden changes in the type of food given. A continuous and constant diet suits horses best.

Horses can be described as trickle feeders – eating small amounts frequently – but over a given period of time they can eat a large amount: as much as two or three cows, for example. It has been estimated that a horse should eat 2.5% of its own bodyweight each day, so a large pony of about 14.2 hands (147 cm) which might weigh 400 kg needs 10 kg of food. At least half – and preferably all – of this food should be forage: i.e. grass, hay and other types of fibrous vegetation such as lucerne (alfalfa) or good quality straw. Horses are fed concentrates ('hard food') such as oats and mixed feeds or

Fig. 6. Labels on bags of horse food are required to show the ingredients and analytical constituents. Forage-based feeds are more natural for the horse than cereal-based ones.

nuts so that they can obtain more energy in a shorter amount of time. This means they do not have to spend so much time eating, and can be used for work. It also means that they can obtain more energy to perform in a way that they would not need to do in the wild, such as racing or eventing. However, concentrates are often based on cereals with a high starch content, which is not what the horse's system is built for and if care is not taken can cause colic and laminitis.

Grass and other forage can in normal circumstances provide horses and ponies with all the nutrients they need. The nutrients required are as follows:

- *Carbohydrates* – either simple (sugar and starch, which provide heat and energy) or complex (cellulose and lignin from plant walls, providing fibre which also produces energy).
- *Proteins* – the building blocks of body tissue, needed particularly by youngsters and breeding horses.
- *Fats and oils* – which also provide energy, and are needed most by horses in hard work and those which are naturally thin.
- *Vitamins, minerals and trace elements* – deficiencies in any of these can cause mental as well as physical problems.

However, as described in Chapter 2, pastures differ and some may be able to provide the whole range of nutrients, whereas in others supplementary feeding may be required.

Unlike many other animals, horses need a high fibre diet but seldom require high protein – although what protein they receive should be good quality (excess protein is thought not to cause problems). They only need 7 to 8.5% of 'crude protein' (foals and yearlings need up to twice as much). The percentage is the fraction of their total intake of dry matter: in other words all their food with the water taken out. If you look at the manufacturer's label on any bag of horse food (fig. 6) you will see a list of ingredients, plus the analytical constituents (including protein and fibre). Elsewhere on the bag you may find an estimate of the amount of digestible energy (DE). This is a measure of the nutritive value of the food, and means the amount of energy that the horse can get from its food. It is measured in joules or megajoules (MJ), and a horse requires between 7 and 12 megajoules of digestible energy for every kilogram of food.

Of course, pasture is not conveniently labelled in this way, but a large enough area of diverse grassland can provide horses and ponies with everything they need. Grassland can provide the following:

- Fibre: 20–40% in dry matter.
- Carbohydrates: 4–30% in dry matter.
- Digestible energy: 8–10 MJ/kg in dry matter.
- Crude protein: 7–20% in dry matter.

(Remember that between 65 and 85% of vegetation is water, so only up to a third of everything the horse grazes is dry matter.)

In considering what pasture is best it is essential to remember how horses and ponies around the world which live in the wild in feral or semi-feral conditions stay healthy, energetic and in good condition on large areas of sparse, infertile grassland. Feeding too rich a diet can be as bad as feeding a poor one.

GRAZING PREFERENCES

If you watch your horse graze you will see how good he is at selecting exactly what he wants (fig. 7). His nose is forever feeling its way through the vegetation, and his teeth bite off the grass

Fig. 7. Horses can select the particular vegetation they want by using their noses, lips, tongue and teeth, and can graze very close to the ground.

accurately, sometimes only a centimetre from the ground. Anything he takes in which he does not want gets dropped out of the side of the mouth.

Horses have quite clear preferences for different plants, and also for different parts of plants. It is assumed that they use a mixture of taste, smell and experience to select what they want. They have different colour vision from humans, so they can detect differences in shades of green which we probably cannot. They like the youngest, sweetest shoots, and prefer leaves to stems. They do not generally like hairy plants, and they are less likely to eat the flowering heads (though many will eat thistle and dandelion heads) or plants which have very strong smells (for example members of the mint family). They prefer grasses and clovers to other flowering plants. However, when their favourite plants are scarce they will start eating other vegetation, including leaves from trees, gorse and coarser grasses which they would normally avoid.

Because of these preferences, horses tend to return again and again to the patches of grass they like best, and as they can graze so short, they will nip off the newest growth and leave the area as smooth as a lawn. This can lead to certain parts of a pasture being damaged because the vegetation cannot recover, or to certain plants being grazed out altogether.

Horses are more selective in what they eat than either sheep or cattle. When they have open access to a wide range of plants they will only eat up to a third of the different varieties on offer. There have been very few studies to find out which plants they like best and which have the best set of nutrients for them, so ideally they should be given as many species as possible. The grasses and other plants which horses are known to prefer are different from the ones which cattle and sheep like. This is because they graze differently: cattle cannot graze very short, and neither sheep nor cattle can eat the tougher plants which horses can; as already mentioned, horses eat a low protein, high fibre diet whereas cattle and sheep cannot cope with such high fibre.

Grassland farmers like to have two main species in their pastures for sheep and cattle: ryegrass and white clover (fig. 8), which have the right nutrients for sheep and cattle and can be grown productively so there is plenty of grass to fatten the livestock and encourage production of milk and wool. Ryegrass and clover are generally too high in sugars and energy and low in fibre for horses, who do not necessarily know what is good for them; they particularly like white clover, which also contains starch, and are quite happy to eat ryegrass, though it is not one of their favourites. As this is a productive mixture, and particularly if not much else is growing with it, horses may well eat too much of it, and the surplus energy will be stored as fat, and may cause laminitis and other problems connected with obesity.

Only a few species of grass have been tested for their palatability to horses, but two which seem to be generally unattractive to them are meadow foxtail and rough-stalked meadow grass. It has been determined that most horses like crested dogstail, red fescue, timothy, cocksfoot, and some strains of perennial ryegrass, though their preferences change with the stage of growth and the species variety. The same is true

Fig. 8. The distinctive flowering head and shiny leaves of ryegrass (above), the most widespread grass in pastures today, but not the best grass for horses as its high energy value may encourage obesity; leaves of white clover (below), also widespread and best limited to small amounts in horse pasture.

of white clover – they will avidly eat some varieties of this at certain times of year, but at other times will ignore it, and they may never touch other varieties. They generally avoid red clover. Again, very few species of broad-leaved plants – often called herbs or wildflowers – have been tested, but ones which horses are reported to like include sainfoin, dandelion, yarrow and ribwort plantain.

Although there is little scientific evidence, a few useful conclusions can be drawn from the studies which do exist.

- Some horses have much stronger plant preferences than others, and this tends to run in families; preferences may vary between individuals.
- Horses like to graze a mixture of species rather than just one or two (fig. 9).
- Some species (for example, cocksfoot, clover) may be preferred in their young stage and ignored when they are mature, or be grazed more at certain times of year than at others.
- If there is more than one variety of a certain species (for example, the commercially bred varieties of grasses), preferences may differ between the varieties.
- Preference between several species may be very marginal.
- Horses may like species which are not necessarily good for them; they do not automatically know what is best.
- When short of food, horses will eat plants which they would ignore if there were plenty to eat.

The different pasture plants will be considered in more detail in Chapter 2.

Fig. 9. A variety of grasses and wildflowers provides horses with a wide range of nutrients and tastes and is more likely to give them the fibre they need than a grassland containing limited numbers of species.

Fig. 10. Horses resting in their favourite spot will soon result in areas of bare ground.

NATURAL BEHAVIOUR

Horses and ponies at pasture behave in very similar ways to horses and ponies living in semi-wild conditions, such as in the New Forest or in the Camargue area of France. They spend about two-thirds of each day grazing, with periods of rest in between. In the wild they will spend more time grazing when vegetation is scarce – up to 19 hours a day – but have to range a greater distance to find it. In pasture situations, if grazing is short, horses cannot go and find more, so they must be fed extra forage. Concentrates may supply the nutrients they need, but large amounts of fibre are also required to aid digestion and avoid boredom.

Horses and ponies only sleep for about four hours a day, but they may spend longer periods resting. The remaining time is spent in social interactions with other horses, such as mutual grooming and playing or in other behaviour such as rolling or having a good gallop. As horses are herd animals it is important for their mental health to have other horses for company. They often just like to congregate in the shade or by a water trough, swishing flies off each other in the summer and giving each other warmth in the winter. This habit can result in areas of bare ground where they have been standing, and this is where they will also roll, giving themselves a cleansing dust-bath in dry conditions, or plastering themselves with protective mud when the weather is wet and cold (fig. 10).

Even when horses are living in the wild with lots of space, there is one thing they are very particular about. They create special latrine areas where they do all their dunging and urinating. To do this they will specifically move away from the areas they are grazing, and then they will not eat near the area where they have dunged. They are the only grazing animals to behave in this way; though most animals will not eat near their own droppings, no others form these latrine areas. It is thought that one of the reasons why horses do this is for parasite control – i.e. any worm eggs will be deposited in the latrines and the grazing areas will be free from parasites.

This habit of creating latrines can become a problem in a confined pasture, because the latrines spread. Mares and geldings approach the latrine area and may stop to dung once they have reached the edge, and soon the boundary is moving further into the rest of the field. Because the dung and urine contain nutrients which make plants thrive, and because the horses will not eat the vegetation near their droppings, the latrines grow grass and weeds which become long and rank (fig. 11). As a result these areas are sometimes called 'roughs', particularly in contrast to the grazed areas, which may become shorter and shorter and are known as 'lawns'.

If latrines are not controlled they can eventually cover up to 90% of the pasture and leave very little grass for grazing. In these circumstances the horses may be forced by hunger or boredom to graze from the latrines, which not only makes them more likely to pick up parasites but is also unnatural behaviour; it is unfair to the horse to place him in circumstances where he has to do this. (See *latrine management,* pp. 61–3 in Chapter 3.)

There is no doubt that horses and ponies are happiest when they are free to roam in a well-vegetated, safe pasture with other horses. This is their natural habitat in which they can behave as did their wild ancestors in the past – grazing, resting, racing and playing, and being generally sociable with their own kind (fig. 12).

Fig. 11. Horse-grazed pasture from the air, showing the spread of unmanaged latrines (darker patches) across the field.

Fig. 12. A group of horses at liberty to indulge in their natural behaviour in a large field.

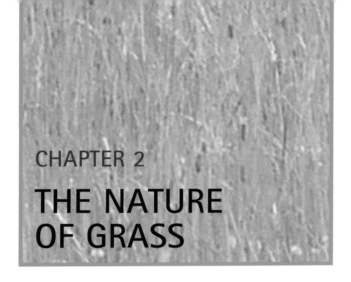

CHAPTER 2

THE NATURE OF GRASS

Grass is the most successful plant on earth. Since it first appeared about 55 million years ago (along with the earliest members of the *Equus* family) it has spread all over the world, and can be found on mountains, seashores, marshes and semi-deserts – everywhere but the deepest Arctic and Antarctic regions. Grasslands cover 40% of the earth's and more than 55% of the UK's land surface. There are 10,000 species of grass world-wide (about 160 in Britain), and the grass family comprises many surprising plants – including bamboo, rice, sugar-cane and the domesticated cereals which form the staple diet of mankind: wheat, barley, oats, maize and rye.

In order to know how to manage grass for horses and ponies it is important to understand how it grows. As the seedling develops it pushes its roots down into the soil, anchoring itself firmly. The roots draw water and the necessary nutrients from the soil up into the stem of the plant, which enables it to grow. The main growth point is at the base, very near the ground, and

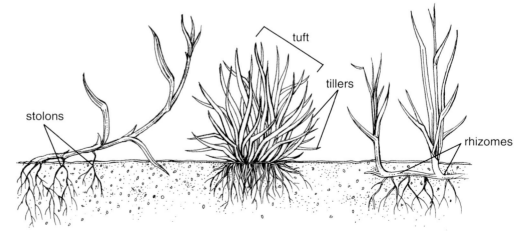

Fig. 13. The grass plant, showing the methods of growth.

from this the stem grows upwards in a series of tubes, joined to each other by nobbly nodes (see fig. 14). Eventually it produces a flowering head, which may be brush-like or tree-like. The leaves arise from the nodes on alternate sides of the stem, and some leaves are also produced from the base of the plant.

Certain grasses are annuals: when they flower and seed, the plant dies, to be replaced by a new plant growing from seed. Most of our pasture grasses are perennials and so the same plant can live for several years. Perennials produce both flowering shoots as described above, and vegetative shoots from the base of the plant. They can produce so many vegetative shoots that they become large, tufty plants. They can also send runners either along the surface of the ground (*stolons*) or underground (*rhizomes*), which produce new shoots and can become separate plants (fig. 13). With this method of growth the perennial grasses do not have to seed in order to survive; they can be cut or grazed and are still able to grow again and to spread out by vegetative means. In fact they respond to being cut or grazed by producing more leafy shoots, which is known as 'tillering'. This is the secret of their success.

The main growing point of the grass plant is very low, just above the surface of the ground, and this protects it from cutting and grazing and allows it to regenerate. In fact, if grass is regularly cut or grazed to between 2.5 and 6.5 cm it is at its most productive, producing more and more leaves and shoots as it is prevented from maturing. If it is left to grow it will put its energy into producing a flower-head and seed, and so

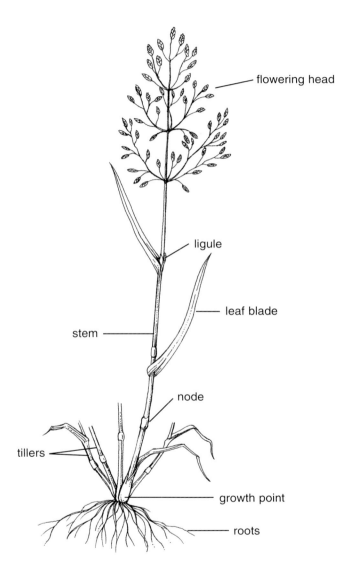

Fig. 14. The grass plant, showing the main parts of the plant.

will produce fewer leaves and provide lower quality forage. However, if grass is constantly grazed very short the growing point can be weakened and the plant will eventually die.

Grasses will flower at different times of year, depending on the species. In Britain the earliest time of flowering is generally around the end of March. Some species continue flowering into November, but most of them produce their flower-heads and seeds from May to July. Once they have flowered and the seed has fallen, they are less nutritious than before they have flowered. Having a range of grasses with different flowering times means that the goodness of the pasture lasts for a longer time over the season.

CHARACTERISTICS OF GRASS

It is important to be able to recognise the main pasture plants. It helps you to know whether you are producing the right pasture for your horse, or whether your management could be improved. At first it might seem impossible to tell one grass from another because they all seem to look the same. But by examining and comparing the common grasses you can quickly see the differences, which can also be a lot of fun. It is easiest to identify grasses from their flowering heads, but some are simple to recognise just by examining the leaves and stem. Before looking at the most common and useful grasses for horse pasture, here are a few features of the grass plant which will help you to distinguish between them (fig. 15). NOTE: It is an offence to uproot a wild plant without the permission of the owner or occupier of the land, so if you are not on your own property, ask first.

SHAPE OF HEAD This can either be brush-like (*spikes*), with the little individual flower-holders (*spikelets*) growing directly on the stem or on very short stalks; or tree-like (*panicles*), where branches come off the main stem, and then the spikelets are attached to the branches by stalks.

FLOWERS The spikelets, which are basically the flower-holders, are usually easy to see, but the actual flowers (*florets*) within them can be hard to distinguish without the help of a magnifying lens. In some species the spikelets only hold one floret, whereas in others they can hold several.

AWNS These are little bristles which may be attached to the floret, and vary in length from less than 0.5 mm to as much as 60 mm.

LIGULE The leaf blade arises from a sheath enclosing the stem. Where the blade and sheath meet there is a tiny transparent membrane called the ligule, which can be long or short, blunt, pointed or jagged. In rare cases there is just a fringe of hairs. If you pull the leaf slightly away from the stem it is easier to see this membrane; a magnifying lens may also help.

AURICLE In some grasses (for example ryegrass), just at the point where the ligule occurs, the leaf may have little outpoints or arms which stick out and clasp the stem.

LEAF The leaf blade can be of various widths or it can be rolled and needle-like. Blades are frequently spear-shaped, narrowing to the tip, and all have parallel veins running the length of the leaf. In some grasses the veins are more distinct than in others, and may seem to form furrows; also, blades may seem to be folded down the centre ('keeled').

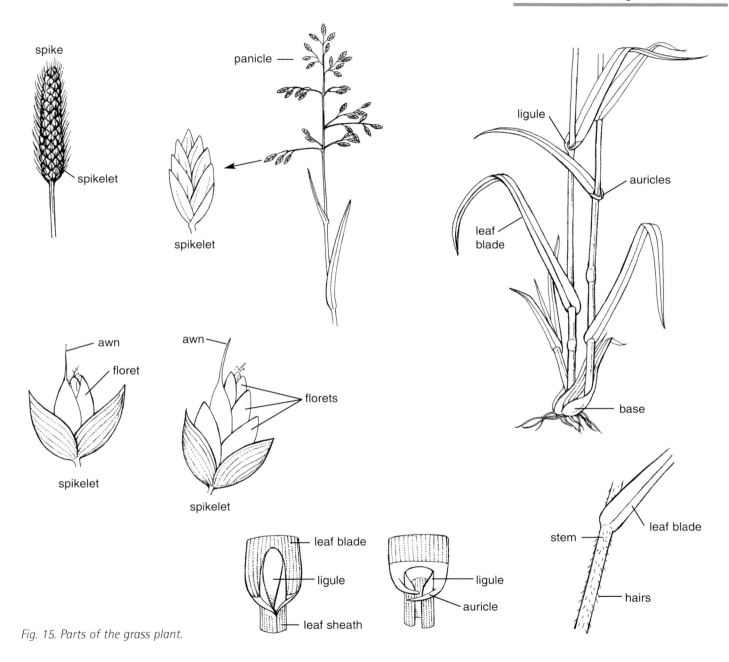

Fig. 15. Parts of the grass plant.

BASE It is often helpful to look at the very bottom of the grass plant, just above the roots, as an identification aid. This part may be a certain colour, or swollen, or there may be distinctive hairs. It is therefore important to pick the whole plant from the roots when trying to identify it (remember, it is an offence to do so without the land owner's permission).

HAIRS Some grasses are very soft and hairy; others have just a few hairs; some have none at all. The frequency and placing of the hairs can make it possible to tell which species of grass you are looking at.

PASTURE GRASSES, THEIR USE AND IDENTIFICATION

Using the above features you should be able to decide what the main grasses in your pasture are. Obviously if your pasture is always being grazed, not many grasses will have a chance to flower. To deal with the problem, you might fence off a typical section of the pasture in the spring (a square metre will do, but make sure that the fence is safe for the horses) and allow the grasses to flower.

RYEGRASS

This is the most common grass in modern pastures, and the one that farmers like best for sheep and cattle, but it is not always the best grass for horses. It is very easy to identify at all stages of growth, and if you only learn to identify one grass this should be it (fig. 16). When it is flowering there is only

Grasses in their flowering and vegetative states, with close-ups of spikelets and ligules (pp. 24–34).

Fig. 16. Ryegrass.

one other common grass with which it can be confused, and that is couch (fig. 17), a weed grass sometimes found in flowerbeds. The difference is that the little spikelets on ryegrass lie flat across the stem from one another, clearly alternating up the stem; if you were to put the stem between the leaves of a book and flatten it you would still be able to see all the flowers clearly. With couch the spikelets face the stem and though they alternate they are much closer and overlap; if you pressed a stem of couch in a book – so that you could see the whole flower – you would only be looking at the spikelets up one side of the stem. Couch is often slightly hairy.

The leaves of ryegrass are very bright green, shiny and fairly rigid, almost as if they were made from plastic. There are fine lines running along the top surface of the leaf, with a deep central line, but the back of the leaf is smooth except for the central 'keel'. To continue the boat analogy, the tip of the leaf looks like the prow of a rowing boat. The ligule is short and there are narrow auricles clasping the stem.

When the grass is not flowering, the main stem where it emerges from the leaves is flat and folded – rather than round as in many other grasses. The stem nearest the root is a rich red, especially when the plant is young; later it may be covered by a dead brown leaf-sheath.

Fig. 17. Couch.

Fig. 18. Crested dogstail.

CRESTED DOGSTAIL

This grass used to be very common but is now more unusual. Studies have shown it to be one of the favourite grasses of horses, and as it is nutritious without being too full of sugars it deserves a place in every horse pasture. Its leaves and stem are not unlike a more delicate ryegrass, but its flowering head is, again, very easy to distinguish from most other grasses (fig. 18). It is an attractive one-sided spike, flat on one side and with all the spikelets on the other. The flower-head is 3 to 5 cm long, to be compared with ryegrass which varies from 4 to 20 cm.

The leaves of crested dogstail are fairly short, shiny underneath, and often appear to be crimped halfway along. The leaf sheaths do not reach very far up the stem: in other words there is quite a distance between the last leaf and the flowering head. The ligule is short and blunt and there are no auricles.

When the grass is not flowering, it is hard to tell whether the main stem is flat or round, but the base of the plant is yellowish and it has hairy yellow roots.

COCKSFOOT

Cocksfoot is the easiest grass of all to identify, in both its flowering and vegetative states (fig. 19). It is useful in pasture, though there should only be a small percentage because horses are not as keen on the mature plant as on the young one. If there is too much of it they will not be able to graze it all, so it will get old, coarse and unpalatable and may spread too much.

The name is derived from the similarity of the flower-head to a cock's foot, with three distinct tufts representing the three toes; it is the only grass which has this type of head. It is robust, able to grow up to 1 metre in height, with wide somewhat stiff and generally pale or grey-green leaves which have a central groove. The ligule is large and long and obviously jagged.

The base of the plant is very white, large and unmistakeably flat rather than round, thus enabling a very certain identification, even when it is not flowering. In its vegetative state the stem emerging from the leaf-sheath is also flat.

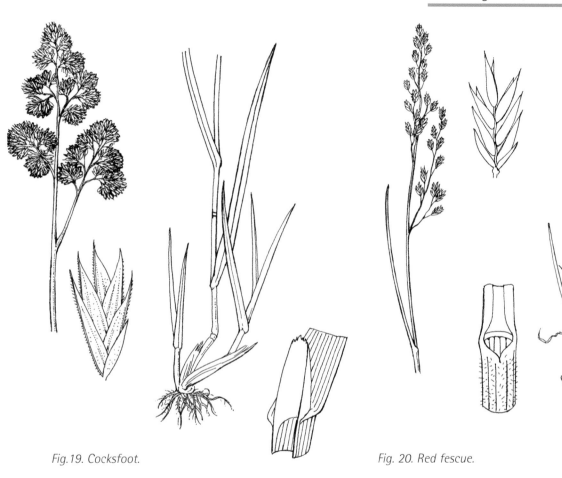

Fig.19. Cocksfoot.

Fig. 20. Red fescue.

RED FESCUE

Red fescue is a particularly widespread grass, being found on most soils and in many different landscapes, from wet and boggy lowlands to mountainsides and sea cliffs. Horses show a preference for it, and the seed of various related species and subspecies of red fescue – mainly creeping, strong creeping and Chewings' – is often included in horse pasture mixes to increase longevity and drought resistance.

It is a tufty grass with needle-like leaves (very similar to its close relative, sheep's fescue, which is mainly found on poor, well-drained soils and semi-natural grasslands – see *Types of Grassland*, p. 41), except for the leaves on the flowering stem which are flat and slightly hairy (fig. 20). The flower-head takes a tree-like form, with the long narrow spikelets standing erect at the end of the branches, and sporting short awns. Although the leaves and the flower-head are fine, the plant can be quite robust and up to 80 cm in height.

The needle-like leaves are the most obvious feature of the vegetative plant, as it does not have much of a ligule. The base of the plant is sometimes reddish, but not as obviously so as ryegrass. It can have creeping roots and over-ground runners.

MEADOW FESCUE

This is a productive grass and can be dominant in the sward, but it is a good grass for horses – perhaps less appropriate for native ponies which require less fertile pastures.

The flower-head looks like a larger, stouter version of red fescue, with many more branches but without the awns on the spikelets (fig. 21). The leaves, however, are always flat and can be up to 4 mm wide. The ligule is short and there are auricles, which can make the vegetative plant look similar to ryegrass, but the leaves are longer than ryegrass and have rough edges.

SMOOTH MEADOW GRASS

Known as 'Kentucky Blue Grass' in the USA, it is not as favoured by horses as was once thought, but is the best of the Meadow Grasses and useful for its turf-forming properties. It is often short, from 15 cm, but can grow to 80 cm tall.

The flowering head is tree-like, in the shape of a pyramid, with spikelets which are stout and short, particularly when compared with red fescue or the Bent Grasses. The ligule is short and collar-like. The leaves of Meadow Grasses are

Fig. 21. Meadow fescue.

very distinctive, with parallel sides and two parallel lines ('tramlines') running down the centre, and ending in a hooded tip which looks like the prow of a rowing boat (fig. 22).

Smooth meadow grass has creeping rhizomes underground, and can have hairs at the base of the leaf blade. The stem emerges flattened from

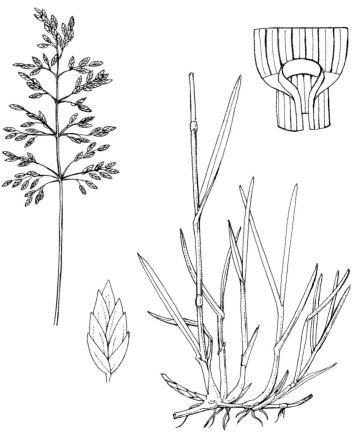

Fig. 22. *Smooth meadow grass.*
the leaf sheath in the non-flowering plant.

ROUGH MEADOW GRASS

Rough meadow grass is very similar to smooth meadow grass in appearance (fig. 23). It is a reasonably useful grass in horse pastures, for although it is not a favourite grass of horses it has good turf-forming characteristics. It appears very easily on its own from the seed bank so there is seldom cause to include it in a seed mix.

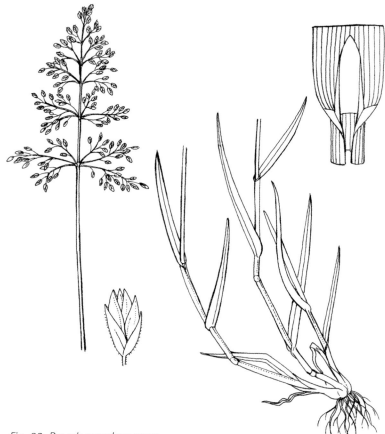

Fig. 23. *Rough meadow grass.*

The 'rough' and the 'smooth' descriptions of these two Meadow Grasses refer to their stems, and although the difference is quite subtle you can feel it if you rub the stem against your chin, just below your lower lip. Rough meadow grass has leaves very similar to smooth meadow grass, though they are broader at the base. It has a long, pointed ligule on the main stem and is often a bright green as opposed to the greyer green of its

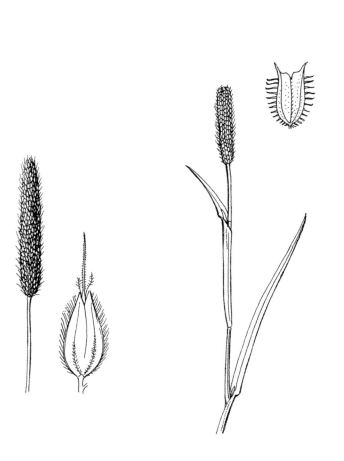

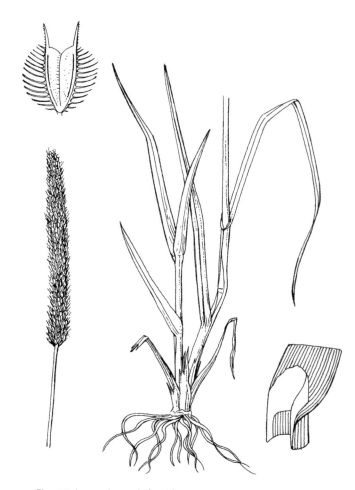

Fig. 24. Meadow foxtail.   Fig. 25. Small-leaved timothy.   Fig. 26. Large-leaved timothy.

relation. It spreads by above-ground stolons.

TIMOTHY

Timothy, particularly the lower-growing, smaller varieties, is an excellent grass for horses. It is low in sugar but winter hardy, and can provide good ground cover.

It has a brush-like head, hard to mistake for any other common grass except meadow foxtail (fig. 24). Meadow foxtail, which is not liked by horses, flowers early in the season (April–June) as opposed to the late heading date of timothy (June–August), and this is a good guide to which is which. There are two native species of timothy – small-leaved (sometimes called cat's-tail) and features (figs. 25 and 26). Usually the flowering head is 1–6 cm long on the smaller variety and up to 15 cm on the large one. Some bred varieties of timothy have even longer flowering heads and are generally bigger plants. Bred varieties which are higher in carbohydrates should be avoided in horse pastures.

Identifying timothy in the vegetative state takes a bit of practice but it soon becomes readily recognisable. The ligules are slightly pointed (more so in small-leaved timothy), and the blue-green leaves clearly taper from a broad base, and are quite short in the small-leaved variety and held erect. The base of the plant is often swollen and brown.

YORKSHIRE FOG

This attractive grass is not much liked by horses except in its youngest stage, but it grows readily, especially on damper or disturbed pastures. It is soft and hairy, and the flowering head looks brush-like when young but then opens up to a tree-like shape, which is often pink to purplish. This is an easy plant to identify in its vegetative state, not only because of its hairiness but because the base of the stem is striped red and white (sometimes jokily referred to as 'pink pyjamas'). The ligule is medium length and blunt (fig. 27).

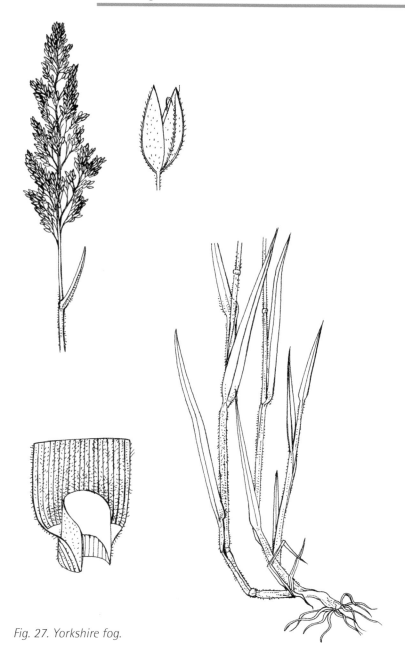

Fig. 27. Yorkshire fog.

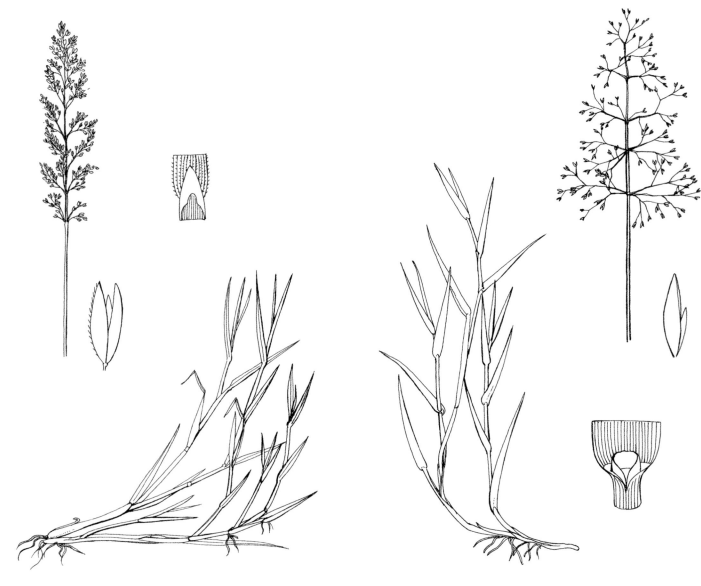

Fig. 28. Creeping bent (left) and common bent (right).

and blunt (fig. 27).

CREEPING AND COMMON BENT

Creeping bent and its close relative common bent are often dismissed as pasture grasses for other livestock, but horses are happy to eat them and in the past creeping bent (known then as 'fiorin') was thought to be a valuable grass for horses. It is good in pasture because it will form a good turf in poor conditions, but it does not need to be included in seed mixes as it will usually appear of its own accord.

The bent grasses flower later than many, starting in July, and the flowering heads look fine and dark in comparison to other tree-like flower-heads such as fescues or meadow grasses. The spikelets are numerous and very small and fine, and when young they are held clustered and erect on the branches, which later drop to a more tree-like form. The leaves are smooth and pointed, and tend to be loose rather than firm (fig. 28).

Creeping bent has a long ligule and is often bent at the base, which is the easiest way to distinguish it from common bent. It is not always an easy grass to identify in its vegetative state.

FALSE OAT GRASS

This grass may be found growing in latrine areas but would not normally be present in a well-managed pasture as it does not like being grazed or regularly cut. Horses do not particularly like it. The tree-like flower-head is large (10-25 cm long) and loose, with noticeable awns which are often bent, giving it an untidy appearance. The easiest way of identifying the plant in its vegetative state is by the often swollen, orange base of the stem which

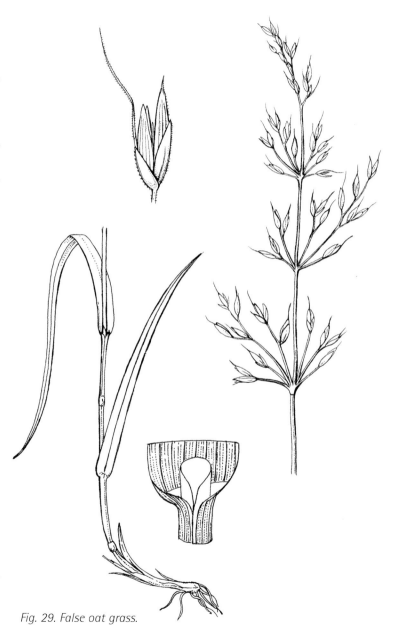

Fig. 29. False oat grass.

The grasses discussed in this chapter are the most common grasses to be found in pasture, but if you graze an old-established pasture you could have 15 or 20 different grasses altogether. If you have a poorly managed pasture which turns to mud every winter you are likely to have annual 'weed' grasses such as sterile and soft brome (figs. 30 and 31), which are of little value.

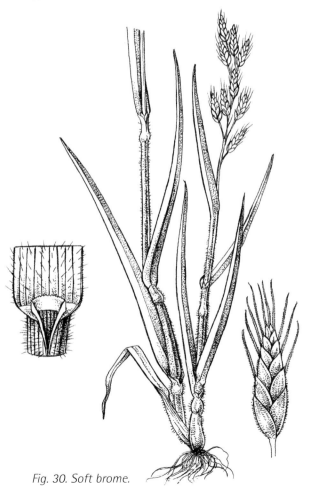

Fig. 30. Soft brome.

Fig. 31. Sterile brome.

WHAT GROWS WHERE

If you have been looking at your pasture and identifying grasses, you will know that there is more than just grass growing in it, and it is important to remember that grasslands contain a whole range of plants (fig. 32): as well as the grasses, there are many other flowering plants

Fig. 32. A grassland community consisting of a variety of grasses, rushes (back right), and wildflowers (including red and white clover and buttercups, bottom left, and orchids, centre).

whole range of plants (fig. 32): as well as the grasses, there are many other flowering plants which are variously called wildflowers, herbs or weeds, depending on what you are looking for! There may also be rushes and sedges, particularly if the ground is a bit damp, and mosses and lichens. This assemblage of plants is called a 'grassland community'.

The plants which grow together in a grassland community are not just an arbitrary selection but grow together for a reason. Different communities will be found in different conditions, whether these are natural – such as soil type, climate or altitude – or man-made, created by different types of management.

CLIMATE

The climate has a direct effect on the growth of

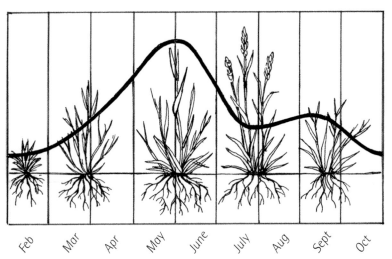

Fig. 33. The typical pattern of grass growth in Britain, with the fastest growth taking place in late spring and early summer, a second peak in early autumn, and little growth over the winter.

grass. Grass grows best when rainfall averages between 500 and 1500 mm per year, and when the temperature is between 5 and 20 degrees Celsius. Rainfall and temperature affect the species that will grow, with for example some better adapted to dry conditions and some to wet. The climate of Britain is very good for grass growth, but because it is fairly similar across the whole country it does not have a great effect on what grows where.

However, in response to rainfall and temperature the grass does not grow evenly throughout the year but starts slowly in about March, and is at its peak by May and June, when there is often more good quality grass than horses can cope with. It levels off in July and begins to decline with drier weather. There is a second spurt of growth in September, before it slows to a virtual standstill in October or November (fig. 33). This pattern of growth can be evened out by setting some land aside for hay in the most productive months, cutting it between mid-June and August, and using it for feed through the winter months when growth is very slow.

SOIL

The soil has more effect than climate on grass growth in Britain. It is formed from the underlying rocks (for example granite in Scotland, red sandstone in Devon and limestone in the Cotswolds), and frequently from materials brought in by glaciers or rivers in previous ages – boulder clay, alluvial till and gravels (fig. 34). Soils are made up of minerals (from the rock), organic matter (the remains of living things, both plant and animal) and pores (the spaces between the soil particles) (fig. 35). The pores contain air and water, and the soil is also full of living organisms, ranging from bacteria to earthworms, all of which play a part in the formation and maintenance of the soil.

The characteristics of soil which govern what grows where are its alkalinity, its drainage qualities and its inherent fertility.

Alkalinity refers to how acid the soil is, and is measured by the concentration of hydrogen ions (pH). Measurement is on a scale of 0 to 14, from acid to alkaline (if you have used litmus paper you may remember it goes red for acid, green for neutral and blue for alkaline). In Britain the most acid soils have a pH of about 4, and the most alkaline (sometimes called calcareous, after chalk soil which is strongly alkaline) are about 8.5. Grass grows best at a pH between 5 and 6.5 (7 is neutral). Acid, neutral and alkaline soils will generally support different grassland communities: some plants, for example, can only tolerate alkaline soils; others may not be able to grow on acid soils.

The *drainage qualities* of the soil are largely governed by its texture: i.e. the size of the mineral

Fig. 34. Some soils which show clearly the influence of the underlying rocks: red sandstone (above) and chalk (below).

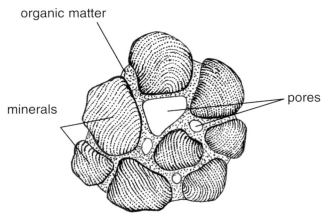

Fig. 35. Soil consists of minerals, organic matter, and pores – spaces which contain air and water as well as living organisms.

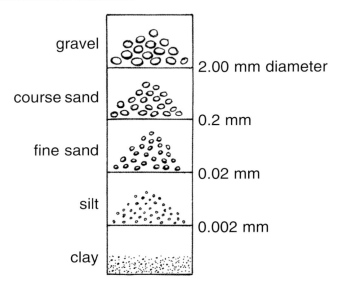

gravel

2.00 mm diameter

course sand

0.2 mm

fine sand

0.02 mm

silt

0.002 mm

clay

Fig. 36. The mineral particles of soil and their relative sizes. Imagine that each division is a sieve with smaller and smaller holes, allowing the smallest particles through to the bottom but trapping the larger ones in their appropriate categories.

Fig. 37. A clay soil which has become compacted in winter by too much treading in wet weather (made worse by the feeding areas), leading to water standing on the surface and unable to drain away through the compacted soil.

particles which are among its main constituents and which range from very fine clay particles through silt to sand (fig. 36). Sandy soil is coarse, like that found on beaches, but is not as coarse as gravel. Clay particles are fine and sticky and in wet conditions will cling together, causing the soil to hold a lot of water which only drains away slowly. If wet clay soils are put under pressure from hooves or machinery the particles will cling together even more, the pore spaces will be squeezed out, the soil will become compacted, and water will be unable to pass through it (fig. 37). At the opposite extreme, water runs quickly through sandy soils. Thus when there is little rain the sandy soil cannot hold on to the moisture and it quickly becomes dry and parched. On the other hand, when it is wet it drains well, unlike the easily waterlogged clay soil.

The *fertility* of the soil – how well it can feed the vegetation growing in it – is closely related to drainage qualities. Plants take up nutrients with the soil water, so if the soil can hold water like a sponge there will be plenty of nutrients available and the soil will be fertile. If the water runs though quickly, there will be few nutrients for the plants. This means that clay soils are naturally more fertile, allowing better growth than sandy soils. However, constantly water-logged soils deprive the plant of oxygen and it will not be able to make use of the nutrients, so the right balance is required.

The amount of organic matter in the soil can also affect both drainage and fertility. Organic matter (decayed vegetation and animal remains) can hold water and nutrients, and will improve

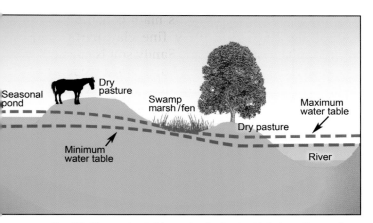

Fig. 38. The water table varies in its depth below the surface, and the ground will be marshy where it is always close to the surface or just above.

sandy soils; it will also improve clay soils by making them less liable to compaction, so water will be less likely to sit on the surface and more likely to filter through the soil. Where there is high organic matter, there will be more soil organisms – for example, dung beetles, earthworms, fungi, bacteria and other forms of life living in the soil, all of which help to improve soil structure and available nutrients. Organic matter is particularly important for horse pastures, as it forms a thick springy turf to lessen the impact on galloping hooves.

If the water table is high and the soil is frequently waterlogged from below, the ground will become marshy (fig. 38). There are many different names for marshy ground – e.g. swamp, mire, bog, fen – depending on how wet it is and whether the soil is acid, alkaline or neutral. If wet conditions over long periods prevent the normal decay of organic matter because of lack of oxygen, peat soil is formed. Many wet areas are based on peaty soils.

SUCCESSION

Different plant communities will grow in all these different conditions – wet or dry grasslands of different soil types and pH. To find out more about what grows where, look at the process of vegetation formation, starting with bare ground. If you take a typical piece of bare ground, such as a badly trodden ('poached') gateway, and leave it undisturbed for a while, new plants will gradually appear. These are generally annual species – flowers and grasses which can establish easily from seed. They are often thought of as weeds because they are quick to grow in areas where they are not necessarily wanted.

As time goes by and the area remains undisturbed, different plants will arrive by seed or by vegetative spread, and perennial flowers and grasses will be established. To begin with, they might be docks and thistles, particularly if the area is quite fertile. There will generally be some grasses and flowers which are more successful than others, the 'dominant' species which take advantage of the nutrients in the soil more quickly than other plants, growing tall and crowding the others out. The more fertile the soil, the more likely this is to happen. On less fertile soil there is likely to be a large number of different species, growing slowly because there are fewer nutrients to go round and no one species can get enough to overtake the others.

In Britain if an area of grassy vegetation is left completely undisturbed for a few years, a new

Fig. 39. Stages of succession: (top left) new grass and seedlings on bare soil; (bottom left) mature grass and wildflowers with a regular programme of grazing and cutting; (above) undergrazed grass with dead tussocks and woody shrubs.

range of plants will begin to establish themselves: woody, shrubby species such as hawthorn and wild rose. Eventually bigger tree species will appear, such as birch and ash, and after many years the bare patch will have turned into a forest. This whole process is called **succession** (fig. 39).

If at the stage of grassy vegetation the area is grazed or cut, the woody species will not become established. This is what happens to all the grass throughout the country: it is being regularly grazed, or cut for hay or silage, or mown – for lawns, parks and playing fields or just to keep it tidy. How it is managed will also affect what grows: some species will grow in hay meadows but will not tolerate being grazed; other species thrive on being cut several times a year, and so on.

It is thus evident that grassland management is of great importance for our whole landscape and the nature of the countryside.

TYPES OF GRASSLAND

There are many different grassland communities across the British Isles. Those which have been undisturbed for years, perhaps even centuries, except for grazing and cutting, are known as 'semi-natural' grasslands (they are not 'natural', because to remain as grass they need to be grazed or cut). The best semi-natural grasslands for horse grazing are on chalk and limestone, where the vegetation is full of calcium for forming strong bones and the soils are not very fertile. As explained in Chapter 1, horses do well on the low protein, high fibre vegetation which is found on these less fertile soils. Also, as mentioned previously, a wider variety of species grows on less fertile soils, particularly on alkaline ones, so there is a greater range of plants available to give horses the nutrients they need.

Our native ('semi-feral') ponies live on a variety of semi-natural grassland types, from the moors of Dartmoor and Exmoor to the hills of Wales and Scotland, as well as the wet grass and woodlands of the New Forest (fig. 40). Ponies are now also used to graze special wetland areas such as the Fens of East Anglia. In all these areas they roam over many hundreds of acres of grass without becoming obese or contracting laminitis. It is being confined to 'managed' grasslands which causes problems.

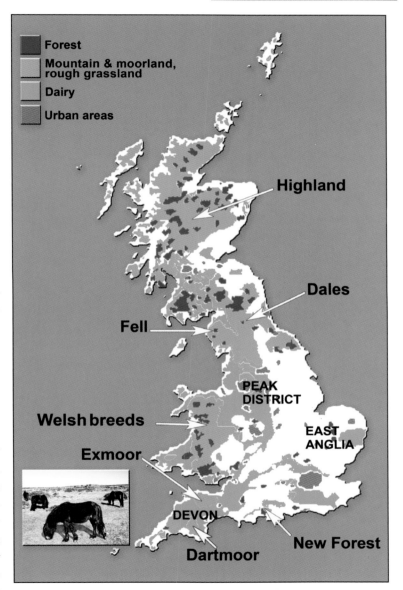

Forest

Mountain & moorland, rough grassland

Dairy

Urban areas

Highland

Dales

Fell

PEAK DISTRICT

EAST ANGLIA

Welsh breeds

Exmoor

DEVON

New Forest

Dartmoor

Fig. 40. The mountains and moorlands of Britain, also showing areas of rough grasslands and dairying, and the original homes of Britain's native ponies.

As well as grazing and cutting, many different management techniques are applied to grassland, such as drainage, fertiliser, chemical sprays and even ploughing up and re-seeding. Management also has an effect on what grows where.

Most grassland in Britain is used for sheep and cattle grazing (or for making hay and silage for these animals). For centuries farmers have worked to make their grassland more productive so that they can maintain as many animals as possible, which will quickly put on weight ready for market, or produce good quality milk or wool. To achieve this, the fields need to be full of the most nutritious grass species rather than the wide range of plants found in semi-natural grasslands. The hayfields need to be easy to cut and quick to dry, and to produce as much growth as possible. The silage fields must produce growth quickly so that it can be cut more than once a year, starting as early as May. Management techniques are therefore applied which will make the fields grow evenly and productively, and which counteract the natural differences described above of the underlying rocks on the vegetation. The farmers are happy if their fields contain just a few species, preferably ryegrass with perhaps some white clover. There are sure to be other species too, but they will be small and insignificant.

More than half of the land area of the UK is agricultural grassland (fig. 41). This includes the mountain and moorland areas of Devon, Wales, the Peak District, and the Scottish Highlands, which are all managed by grazing with sheep, cattle or ponies, and are also grazed by wild animals such as deer, rabbits and hares. Most of the remaining lowland grassland is 'improved', the term used for grasslands that have been managed for increased production. About a quarter of the rest of the land area consists of agricultural crops and woodland, and the remaining quarter is urban (towns and villages), roads, airports etc. This clearly demonstrates how important grassland is in the landscape of Britain. Along with the small amount of woodland, it forms our countryside, and is where our wildlife lives. Horses and ponies graze about 1 million hectares of the agricultural grasslands – that is about 10% – so the way horse pastures are managed has an important effect on the

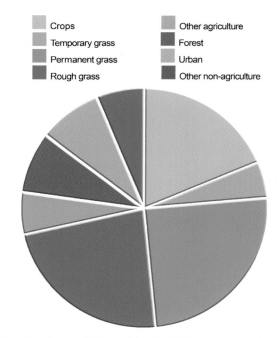

Fig. 41. How land is used in the UK (percentage of total land area in 2007). The various types of grassland total more than half the land area of the country.

Fig. 42. Weed-infested pasture, with overgrazed grass and bare patches and a poor dividing fence. Not only is this unsightly but it poses a danger to the horses, both from the ragwort and from worms and poor nutrition.

landscape, and on the number and distribution of plants species, insects and other wildlife.

HORSES IN THE LANDSCAPE

All too often, people who keep horses are criticised for their pasture management, and unfortunately the criticism is sometimes justified. Many horse pastures are not properly looked after: they are overgrazed in summer and badly poached in winter, so instead of a close sward of grasses and flowers, all that grows is a range of weeds amid bare patches of ground (fig. 42). Not only is this unsightly, it is also bad for the soil, which can become compacted or may even be blown or washed away in bad weather. If soil washes into ditches or streams it takes with it nutrients which pollute the water, causing problems both for the wildlife which lives in it and for us humans, because the pollutants have to be removed before the water can re-enter the drinking water system. Also it is the best topsoil that blows or washes away, leaving the pasture less able to support good vegetation. Weeds, which are very likely to include thistles, docks and ragwort, seed and spread not only into the rest of the pasture but also into neighbouring fields and crops. Unmanaged

Fig. 43. Poor fencing, which could easily cause damage to horses as well as looking untidy and unprofessional.

latrine areas grow more weeds, especially nettles, and make the pasture look even messier.

As well as untidy grass, the fencing is sometimes an eyesore (fig. 43). Posts and rails may be broken and patched up, wire sagging or wound around trees, and though electric fencing can be very successful for horses, miles of flapping white tape does not add to the appearance of the countryside. In fact, even a smart post and rail fence may look wrong in some areas – for example on a visible hillside which has no natural field boundaries.

But the other extreme – grass like a croquet lawn, surrounded on all sides by horse wire or post and rail fencing, and the droppings picked up daily – may also be unsatisfactory (fig. 44). Though sometimes thought to be the best management, it often indicates overgrazed pasture. Also it must be remembered that more than just horses and ponies inhabit the field. In a world where many species of wildlife are struggling to survive, it is our responsibility to try and provide food and habitat for them also. All sorts of creatures make their home in grassland, and nearly all of them live in harmony with horses.

If we encourage flowering plants in our pastures, bees and butterflies (fig. 45) will take nectar and pollen, and bees return the service by pollinating the crops and fruit needed for our survival. Butterflies lay their eggs on a variety of grassland plants, including thistles and nettles. Grasshoppers and crickets especially like the varying heights of vegetation found in grazed grassland, and beetles live in patches of bare ground and recycle dead plant materials back into the soil. Horses' droppings attract many crawling and

Fig. 44. Grass as smooth as a lawn may look neat and tidy but is not providing for the horses and is detrimental to the health of the soil, the vegetation and wildlife.

Fig. 45. Bees and butterflies will be attracted to flowering plants in the pasture and need areas of uncut vegetation to lay eggs and make their nests.

flying insects, which help to break down the manure and return nutrients to the soil.

Insects are eaten by many small mammals which live in grassland. They are vitally important as food for bats, which are protected in Britain because most of the species are endangered. Our smallest bat, the pipistrelle, needs to eat 3000 midges every night! Horse pastures are particularly important for serotine and greater horseshoe bats, which eat some of the insects associated with horse droppings, including dung beetles. Bats need trees or buildings to roost in and landscape features such as hedges, fence lines and ditches to fly along using their echo-location system.

Other small mammals such as shrews, voles and mice build grassy nests at the foot of hedgerows or banks on the edge of pastures. Moles make their presence felt by throwing up molehills (fig. 46), but they present no danger to horses – on the contrary, molehills and anthills in a pasture can be beneficial, as they encourage horses to be surefooted (in Spain, rocky pastures are known to have this effect). Molehills indicate the presence of earthworms, which is a good sign for the health of the soil. Rabbits, however, can live on the edge of pastures and dig holes which can cause injuries to horses stepping into them. If rabbits are present it is a good idea to inspect pastures daily and fill in any holes (fig. 47). Note that rabbits are voracious grass eaters, as are hares and deer.

Hares (fig. 48) do not dig holes but lie up in 'forms' or depressions in the vegetation of larger, open fields. They are very attractive animals, but if there are a lot of them they are competing with your horse for the same food. However, unlike rabbits and deer their numbers are declining so it is worth encouraging them.

Like bats, birds are very reliant on insects, especially when they are feeding chicks in the

Fig. 46. Molehills are a sign of healthy soil and present no problem to horses.

Fig. 47. Rabbits are a danger in horse pasture; where they are present, daily inspection is needed to prevent accidents.

Fig. 48. Hares may be found in larger fields, and should be protected and encouraged as they are a vulnerable species in Britain.

boundaries and with a variety of flowering species. Some birds nest on the ground in larger fields, or at the foot of hedgerows, so care must be taken if the field is cut. Many of these wild bird populations are in decline, and the more they can be provided for in the way of food and nesting habitat the better.

Pastures are part of a wider picture (fig. 49), and what we do with them affects not only our horses but other animals as well as people.

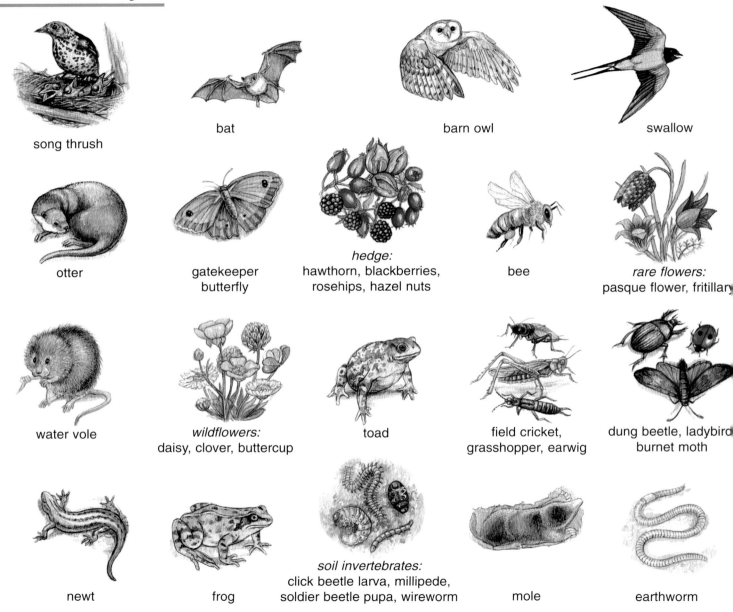

song thrush

bat

barn owl

swallow

otter

gatekeeper
butterfly

hedge:
hawthorn, blackberries,
rosehips, hazel nuts

bee

rare flowers:
pasque flower, fritillary

water vole

wildflowers:
daisy, clover, buttercup

toad

field cricket,
grasshopper, earwig

dung beetle, ladybird
burnet moth

newt

frog

soil invertebrates:
click beetle larva, millipede,
soldier beetle pupa, wireworm

mole

earthworm

Fig. 49. Everything in the pasture is related, and the way we manage it can benefit not only our horses but wildlife, natural resources and ultimately ourselves.

CHAPTER 3
MANAGEMENT OF GRASS

Farmers have great experience in managing grass, especially in producing weed-free, nutritious pasture for sheep and cattle. Many researchers in universities, institutes and commercial companies have studied the best ways of feeding livestock at pasture: which grass species to sow, when to fertilise, what products to use, how to keep the soil drained and in good condition, etc. Much can be learned from this research.

As horses are very different from sheep and cattle, they have different requirements from their pasture. They are athletes, and are not being kept for their meat, milk or wool, so they should not be fattened on lush grasses but should be given large areas of less fertile vegetation to range across. In fact, as described in Chapter 1, their digestive system requires a different diet – lower protein and carbohydrate and higher fibre than either sheep or cattle. They also affect pasture more severely as they run and play (especially if they are shod), create latrine areas and revel in patches of bare ground. They benefit from being out for at least some hours every day

all year round – other livestock is often housed for the whole of the winter. Moreover, horses like different plants and will select a different range of grasses and flowers from cattle or sheep.

'Best practice' agricultural grassland management is therefore not the same as 'best practice' for horses. Many of the techniques are the same, but they need to be used in different ways, as discussed in this chapter.

SOIL

In order for plants to grow well there must be good soil structure, i.e. there must be plenty of pores – the spaces between the mineral particles and organic material of the soil. In a good soil the pores may constitute about 50% of the total volume of soil. Plants can drop their roots down through the pores and find oxygen, water and nutrients several centimetres – sometimes metres – below the surface. Soil organisms such as earthworms use the pores to bring organic matter from the surface down into the soil, enriching it further.

Soil can become compacted if it is run on by heavy machinery (imagine the surface of a permanent track, which can be very hard and possibly even lower than the surrounding ground) or constantly trodden by hooves, especially in wet weather (fig. 50). As it becomes compacted the pores gradually disappear, and it becomes more difficult for roots to push their way into the mass which is formed; water sits on top instead of trickling through, and the soil lacks oxygen. Many horse pastures become compacted, especially if they already lack organic matter in the soil, and particularly on clay soils which stick together very well. The vegetation can only be shallow-rooted and so may be pulled up altogether when grazed, and it lacks natural nutrients as well as air and water for growth.

The soil needs to be kept in good condition, which may mean keeping horses off wet fields in winter and providing alternative areas for exercise. If the soil is already compacted there are mechanical means for relieving the compaction. A *subsoiler* is a machine which drags a hoe-shaped tool underground to loosen up the soil down to about a metre deep, without disturbing the sward too much. *Aerators* and *slitters* (fig. 51) can also help with compaction by breaking up the surface with rotating tines,

Fig. 50. A former fence line where horses have worn a track. Not only has the vegetation been worn away, but the soil has been compacted as shown by the higher level of the land around it. The surface of the track remains damp as water is unable to drain away quickly.

Fig. 51. A slitting machine can help to relieve the problems of surface compaction by creating channels for water, air and soil organisms. More serious compaction may require subsoiling.

Fig. 52. A set of rollers, suitable for hay meadows and newly sown grass but inadvisable for routine use on horse pastures.

allowing water and air to penetrate to the roots of the plants. These disturb the ground less than subsoilers, which will cause 'heave' on the surface, but may be less effective in cases of serious compaction.

Rolling is often undertaken to flatten the soil and to even out the surface, especially if it has become poached over winter; however, it also compacts the soil, so is not recommended on horse pastures. Rollers (fig. 52) can be used on newly seeded pastures and on ungrazed hay fields, but otherwise they will only add to problems of treading. If a poached surface needs to be evened up, this can be better achieved by harrowing.

DRAINAGE

Some soils may easily become waterlogged even when the structure is good, either because they are only slowly permeable to rainfall or because the water table is high. Underfield drainage (fig. 53) helps water to run away more quickly into drainage ditches or watercourses. Some fields, particularly if they have been arable in the past,

Fig. 53. An outlet pipe from underfield drainage, running after a heavy rainfall. Care must be taken that such pipes are kept clear and that ditches are not blocked – so that drainage systems can work correctly.

may already have clay or plastic land drains laid under them. This type of drainage is a major undertaking, consisting of digging deep trenches at intervals across the field and laying pipes, possibly surrounded by gravel. However, it is a long-term solution, provided that the outlet pipe and the drainage ditches are kept sufficiently clear for the water to run out. A simpler alternative is *mole-draining* (fig. 54), where a channel is dug underground by a special machine which leaves just a slit at the surface (rather like a subsoiler). This is far less disruptive and can be very effective, especially if used in conjunction with land drains.

When considering drainage it is essential to take advice from experts. Obviously, if you are going to spend money on such a project it is important for it to work, so a drainage specialist must be consulted. However, you should first take advice from an ecologist or conservation professional, as damp or marshy grassland can be a very special habitat (fig. 55). Drainage can interfere with the wildlife, or cause the irrevocable loss of unusual plant species. You could also be breaking the Environmental Impact Assessment regulations administered by Natural England, which prohibit changes liable to damage natural wildlife habitats. Remember also that water-logged soil – particularly standing water – may be caused by compaction, and relieving the compaction may be required to solve the problem, whereas in these circumstances drains might make no difference.

Fig. 54. Mole drainer, with a close-up of the 'foot' which creates the underground channel.

Fig. 55. Beware of draining wet land without consulting a specialist. This may look like a damp puddle, but it is a Site of Special Scientific Interest (SSSI) because of its marshy vegetation.

RE-SEEDING

If the soil structure is good and the drainage balance natural, there is no reason why the vegetation should not grow well. But if the pasture has been badly managed in the past it may be weedy or contain species which are not the preferred ones for horses. In these circumstances farmers would consider ploughing up the existing grassland and sowing a new sward with the species best suited to livestock. This is generally not recommended for horses, or for grasslands which have a range of desirable species (and which may be liable to an Environmental Impact Assessment).

When grassland is ploughed, three things happen. Many nutrients which were locked in the soil are released; some are lost to the air and the rest will fertilise the new growth for the next few years (this of course is good for farmers who are growing crops on ploughed-up grass fields, but not so good for horses, which may become obese on productive grass). Secondly, the organic matter in the topsoil is pulled up and buried deep; it will have taken many years to build up and is valuable for giving good soil structure and cushioning horse's feet, so an important asset will be destroyed. Finally, seeds which have lain dormant in the seed bank are disturbed and can grow and flower. Unfortunately, the majority of these seeds are usually not desirable species but are more likely to be docks, thistles, rushes and other weeds.

If there are few desirable species in the sward and a lot of weeds, it is not necessary to plough. Instead it is possible to spray out the weeds with a selective weedkiller. After the spray has done its job the field should be harrowed hard to pull out dead material and create bare patches where seed can establish. Note that chemical sprays should be used with great care and not routinely – some people prefer not to use them at all for the sake of the environment.

If there is already a good diversity of grass species, herbs such as yarrow and legumes such as bird's-foot trefoil can be sown into the existing grass. Otherwise a range of grasses which suit the soil type, with or without flower species, should be used. Many off-the-shelf grass mixes for horses will consist of several types of ryegrass (to give a range of flowering times), one or two varieties of red fescue, and maybe timothy or smooth meadow grass. It is preferable, particularly for ponies, to have more of the latter varieties and no ryegrass. If ryegrass is included it should be of the slow-growing, late-heading diploid varieties which are used for sports fields or turf, rather than the productive agricultural varieties. Some very inappropriate ryegrass varieties – particularly those with high sugar content which should never be used for horses – are often included in mixes for horse pasture, and if any ryegrass is included it is essential to know the specific varieties. The mix should also include crested dogstail, one of the favourite grasses of horses, and perhaps a little cocksfoot and meadow fescue if a more productive vegetation is required. Different mixtures are appropriate for different soils, so it is also essential to know what your soil type is. Meters and testing kits for pH (fig. 56) are available at garden centres and are simple to use; or for a more accurate reading (and measurement of nutrient levels as well) you

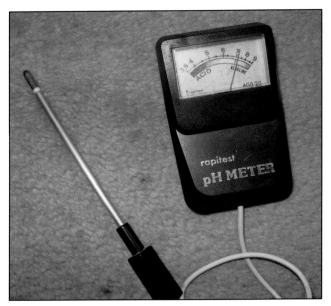

Fig. 56. The type of pH metre which can be bought cheaply at garden centres. The reading will not be as accurate as a laboratory soil test, but it will tell you if your soil is acid, alkaline or neutral.

can send soil samples away to a laboratory to be tested. The table below shows some suitable species for different conditions.

These same mixes can be used for putting former arable land down to pasture. Herbs and legumes suitable for the soil type should be included, but other wildflowers only if there is a good pasture management regime in place, as the seeds are expensive, and one season of overgrazing or poaching will wipe out most of the plants. Equine mixes often include burnet and sheep's parsley, which are unlikely to be successful, as well as yarrow and ribwort plantain ('ribgrass') which are acceptable (fig. 57). Remember that not all plant species will grow well in all soil conditions, and that any mix you sow will end up adapting to the natural conditions, so it is best to start with a mix suitable for the conditions, which will remain in place, rather than an agricultural or ryegrass-based mix which will deteriorate over a few years.

Grasses	Herbs and legumes	Other wildflowers
Basic mix for all soils:	*Basic mix for all soils:*	*For all soils:*
Creeping red fescue	Bird's-foot trefoil	Common knapweed*
Crested dogstail	Yarrow	*For non-acid soils:*
Small-leaved timothy	Ribwort plantain	Cowslip
Smooth meadow grass	*Add on calcareous soils:*	Ladies' bedstraw
Add for more productivity:	Black medick	Salad burnet
Cocksfoot*	Sainfoin	Rough hawkbit
Meadow fescue	*For higher productivity:*	
On poor soils add:	Wild white clover*	
Common bent	Red clover*	

* Use small amounts only

Fig. 57. Ribwort plantain (left) is one of three common plantains, with long blade-shaped leaves and a distinctive flower head; yarrow (right) has white flowers and feathery leaves, and horses will eat it when it is young.

FERTILISER

As described in the previous chapter, grass grows best at a pH of between 5 and 6.5. It also requires a balance of nutrients, in particular nitrogen, phosphorus (phosphate) and potassium (potash), and occasionally other minerals such as magnesium or sulphur. Added to sunlight, water and oxygen this covers everything which any plant needs. Growth is limited by whichever of these factors is the smallest – so if there is low rainfall it may struggle, and if there is not enough potassium it will not reach its full potential. Imagine a car which though full of fuel cannot complete its journey because it has no water in its radiator or no air in its tyres.

When grassland is grazed or cut for hay, some of the nitrogen, phosphorus and potassium which plants have taken up into their leaves to help them grow is removed. Gradually, the reservoir of these elements in the soil is depleted, and they need somehow to be returned to the soil if it is to remain sufficiently fertile to grow more grass. There are various ways in which this happens naturally. Nitrogen occurs in the atmosphere as well as in the soil, and one of the things which happens when lightning strikes is that nitrogen is introduced into the soil from the atmosphere. There is also a family of plants which, through their relationship with soil bacteria growing on their roots, can 'fix' nitrogen from the air and use it for themselves. These are the legumes (fig. 58), most notably white and red clover, but also a range of other clovers, vetches, trefoils and plants such as sainfoin and lucerne (alfalfa).

Other nutrients are returned to the soil through the droppings of the grazing animal, through dead plants left to lie on the sward, through nutrients brought in floods to riverside land, and even through the decaying carcasses of wild animals. Many nutrients can be added by spreading well-rotted farmyard or stable manure, which contains dung, urine and decaying straw or other organic matter. However, it is now most normal to add nutrients through the application of what is known as 'artificial fertiliser', which is

Fig. 58. Members of the family of leguminous plants which can fix nitrogen: sainfoin (top left), bird's-foot trefoil (lower left), red clover (centre), tufted vetch (top right), hop clover (lower right).

an inorganic, manufactured product. Standard off-the-shelf compound fertiliser contains nitrogen, phosphate and potash (NPK) in various proportions, and these are generally used by farmers for applying to grass grazed by sheep and cattle. The three main elements have different functions for the growth of grass:

- Nitrogen gives a fast response in growth of leaf and stem.
- Phosphorus helps plants to root.
- Potassium is needed for flowers and seed.

The use of artificial nitrogen (N) fertiliser is not recommended for horse paddocks. The response of the grass to artificial nitrogen is too pronounced, resulting in a rapid lush growth which is too much for horses and particularly ponies. At this stage of growth the grass is high in soluble carbohydrates and there is plenty of it available, so it is in such conditions that horses and ponies are at risk of laminitis and obesity (*see Chapter 4*). Repeated use of nitrogen will also kill any wildflowers in the sward.

The response of grass to phosphorus and potassium is not quite so rapid, but there is still a difference in use between horse paddocks and fields for sheep and cattle. The amount of phosphorus (P) or potassium (K) in the soil is measured in milligrams per litre of soil, and assigned an index figure from 0 (deficient) to 9 (very high). An index of 2 for both elements is considered the minimum for sheep and cattle. For horses an index of 1 will be sufficient, but for hayfields an index of 2 is preferable.

It is usually not necessary to apply *any* fertiliser, whether organic or artificial, if paddocks are not overgrazed, are rested sufficiently, and if droppings are harrowed in. This will result in more gradual grass growth and moderate productivity. However, there may be circumstances where something does need to be added. This is especially true if hay or haylage is going to be made. Before any action is taken it is advisable to have the soil tested for nutrient levels. P and K, lime and magnesium are generally tested for. Several soil samples from around the field (to about 7.5 cm depth) should be mixed together in a plastic bag and sent to a laboratory for testing. As discussed above, poor grass growth may be the result of compaction or drainage problems rather than a shortage of nutrients.

If grass growth is poor and nutrient levels low, the best approach is to apply farmyard or stable manure, so well rotted that it forms a black tilth. To enable the growing grass to make the best use of the slow release of nutrients, it should be spread at times when there is about to be a spurt of growth – March if it is dry enough (or as early as possible thereafter), or in August (*see Chapter 2*).

Fig. 59. A muck spreader, showing the moving floor and beaters at the back of the machine which throw the muck out on to the grass behind. Compact machines are also available for towing behind a small tractor, Land Rover or ATV.

The advantage of spreading this sort of organic manure is not only the slow, natural release of nitrogen and other elements, but also the increase of organic matter in the soil. Spreading only needs to take place every few years.

There are also disadvantages: manure can be hard to handle, needing specialist machinery (fig. 59) and a lot of time, and the nutrient content is not precise. Fields which have had organic manures applied need to be rested for at least six weeks before grazing again; some experts recommend resting for several months or taking a hay cut before returning to grazing.

If artificial fertiliser is the only option (and it should never be used on pasture grazed by native ponies and others prone to laminitis), extremely low levels of nitrogen should be added, and either a hay crop taken or other stock grazed before horses are allowed back on. For this purpose, semi-organic compound fertiliser with low nitrogen (N) especially manufactured for horse paddocks and available in 20 kg bags can be purchased (fig. 60). It is also possible to apply just phosphorus and/or potassium in different forms and, where possible, products such as Fibrophos or basic slag (which also has a liming effect–*see below*) should be used. Generally P and K applications need take place no more than once in five years.

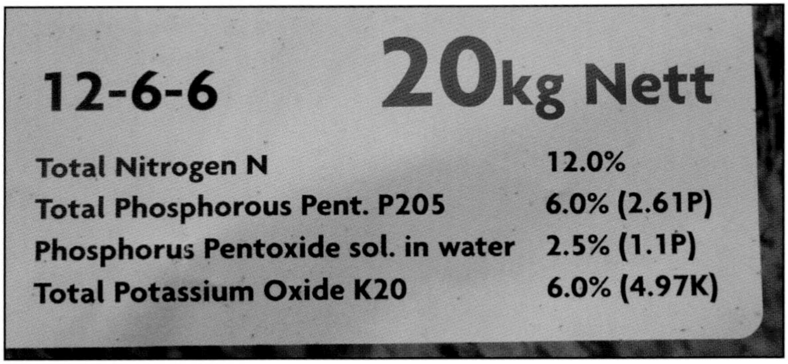

Another substance which can often be applied to horse pasture without detriment is lime. As mentioned above, a neutral pH of about 6.5 enables grass to grow at its best – much higher or lower than this, certain elements will be locked up in the soil and plants are unable to take advantage of them. Lime is highly alkaline, and if it is applied in powder form to soil, it will raise the pH and make acid soil neutral or alkaline for a few years, thus releasing nutrients for vegetation to use. Therefore, if the pH of your soil is low, applying lime once every five or more years will have a beneficial fertilising effect. Be aware that if you have special acid-loving plant species you will destroy them by adding lime. You will need to keep horses off the field until the lime is thoroughly washed in.

A very good way of adding lime is to use calcified seaweed. This contains both lime and trace elements and allows a gentle release of other essential nutrients, and can be applied while the horses are still grazing – any time between February and September.

Before applying any fertilising or liming agents to semi-natural grassland, flower-filled grassland or grass which has never previously

12-6-6	20kg Nett
Total Nitrogen N	12.0%
Total Phosphorous Pent. P205	6.0% (2.61P)
Phosphorus Pentoxide sol. in water	2.5% (1.1P)
Total Potassium Oxide K20	6.0% (4.97K)

Fig. 60. Horse paddock fertiliser containing 12 units of nitrogen and 6 each of phosphorus and potassium (12-6-6, compared to the 20-10-10 of standard compound fertiliser). Although organic based and using slower-release nitrogen, this is still too much, if used at the recommended levels, for many horses (and wildflowers!). It is best used on species-poor hayfields.

been treated, you should take expert advice and you may have to undertake an Environmental Impact Assessment as required by Natural England.

LATRINE MANAGEMENT

As already mentioned, droppings return nutrients to the soil and horses create latrine areas where they do all their dunging and urinating. The urine contains nitrogen and potassium, and the dung contains nitrogen and phosphorus. Because these nutrients are all returned to a small area, the plant growth becomes very lush – and plant species which thrive on potassium, such as creeping thistle, and those which like nitrogen and phosphorus, such as docks and nettles, do particularly well. Because horses no longer want to eat the grass growing near the droppings the whole area becomes rough, the vegetation becomes rank, and then even if the droppings are removed after a few weeks the horses are still not interested in eating the grass.

The usual way of dealing with this is to avoid the formation of latrines by picking up the droppings daily, or at least every three or four days, so that the horse is not put off grazing the patches, and the full amount of nutrients do not get a chance to rot back into the soil. Studies have shown that horses will graze the area if the dung is removed (before rank growth can take place), even if they have urinated in the patches, as it is the smell of the dung rather than the urine which puts them off. However, although picking up droppings has some obvious advantages (appearance, parasite control, maximum grazing use of the paddock), there are also disadvantages.

First of all, the creation of latrine areas is the horse's own method of parasite control. By avoiding grazing anywhere near the dung he is less likely to pick up the worm larvae which are ready and waiting near the dung patches to continue their life cycle within the horse. There are virtually no worm larvae to be found in 'lawns'– the areas where no dunging takes place. When droppings are removed the horse is no longer guided to these special areas and may be at risk of taking in parasites, if droppings have not been picked up quickly enough to prevent the spread of the larvae into the surrounding grass. The life cycle of worms is looked at in more detail in *Chapter 4*.

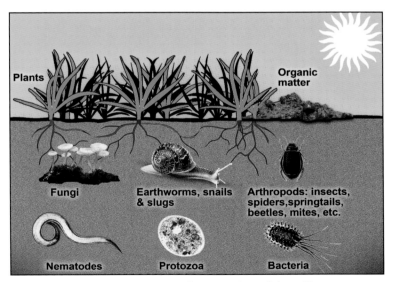

Fig. 61. Soil invertebrates help to improve the soil by taking dead plant material and dung and incorporating it into the topsoil, adding nutrients and structure. Constantly removing droppings will decrease this essential activity.

Fig. 62. Grazing sheep or cattle with horses (at the same time or after each other) is a useful aid to managing latrine areas, as the three species will eat different parts of the vegetation and will help to clear up each other's parasites.

Picking up the droppings also removes most of the nutrients and organic matter which could otherwise be returned to the soil. There are many creatures living in the soil, such as beetles and earthworms (fig. 61), which help to break down droppings, taking particles down into the soil where they rot and not only release nutrients but add to the soil organic matter which is so important for creating a yielding turf for galloping hooves. Constant removal of this material will mean fewer soil invertebrates and a gradually more and more impoverished soil.

As mentioned above, different nutrients are returned to the soil through droppings (phosphorus and also calcium) and urination (potassium and most of the nitrogen), so by removing the droppings an imbalance is created which gradually leads to the acidification of the soil.

However, latrine areas must be controlled in some way, either by picking up the droppings or by other means. If the paddock can be rested, harrowing is the best solution and is discussed below. Another solution is to pick up only some of the droppings, so allowing latrine areas to persist but not to spread. The idea here is that the horses still have a designated area, which must be cut regularly to avoid rank growth, but that picking up droppings at the edge of the area *daily* prevents latrines spreading to take up larger areas of the field. In this case, care must be taken to avoid overgrazing of the lawns so that the horse is not tempted to graze the roughs.

An excellent way of controlling latrine areas – thought not always easy to achieve – is to rotate grazing with other animals (fig. 62). Cattle, sheep and horses will graze near each others' droppings and as they prefer different vegetation will clear up what has not been eaten. They also break the life cycle of each other's parasites (*see Chapter 4*).

There are some situations where droppings should always be picked up: if fields are over-stocked for any reason; if there is more than moderate pressure of grazing on species-rich grassland; if there is any suggestion of a parasite problem; if the look of the field is paramount, for example for an equestrian business; or after

Fig. 63. Droppings from the field should not be piled at the foot of hedges or beside ditches.

using ivermectin based wormers, when droppings should be picked up for at least two weeks (*see Chapter 4* for why this is important).

When disposing of droppings, whether from the field or stable, it is very important to think about where they are going to be piled. Piles of droppings or muck heaps should not be sited alongside hedges or trees, as the concentrated nutrients will eventually kill them (fig. 63). In particular they should not be put by ditches, streams or any other water-carrying feature. This is because the nutrients will be washed out of the droppings and into the water, causing all sorts of problems, both to the quality of the water which is eventually going to be used for drinking and to the vegetation and wildlife that live in the ditch. On farms in most parts of the country it is illegal to pile manure within 10 metres of a watercourse.

HARROWING AND TOPPING

There are ways of increasing the productivity of grass which do not involve any type of fertiliser. One of these is by harrowing. A harrow is a set of spikes on a frame, towed behind a tractor or other vehicle. Harrows used on grassland are generally called 'chain harrows', and the frames are flexible rather than rigid (fig. 64).

The action of harrowing is to pull out dead grass, moss and creeping weeds, allowing more oxygen and light to reach the plants and encouraging grass to spread. It can create small areas of bare ground for seeds to establish themselves (preferably grass and wildflower seeds, not weeds!). If it lightly disturbs the soil, locked-up nitrogen can be released for the use of plants, encouraging growth (but again, if it causes too much disturbance, it can encourage

Fig. 64. *A set of chain harrows, one of the most useful tools for grassland management.*

unwanted weeds). It also breaks open and moves droppings, and spreads cut grass.

Harrowing is a valuable operation in most cases, especially if carried out in the early spring, when dead winter grass needs to be removed and the young grass can utilise the nutrients, or in August, just before the second flush of growth when seeds are trying to establish and plants need further nutrients. However, there are two situations where harrowing must be undertaken with care.

The first is when there are delicate wildflowers in the sward. The action of the harrow may be too strong and may damage or uproot important species. The second is where droppings are left to lie in the field. As mentioned above, harrowing is a good way of controlling the formation of latrine areas. It spreads the droppings and prevents the build-up of nutrients in the roughs. However, the timing of harrowing is important, because spreading the droppings can also spread worms. As well as following a sensible worming programme, spreading droppings in warm, dry conditions will ensure that they break open and dry out, killing the worms and enabling quicker breakdown of the droppings into the soil. Pastures need to be rested for about six weeks after harrowing, as the horses will not want to eat where their droppings have been spread.

Another mechanical operation which increases the productivity of the grass is cutting ('topping') at regular intervals. This may seem surprising, but topping grass during the main growing season (April to July) encourages it to grow more vigorously and to produce more leaves. Grass produces its highest yield if it is regularly cut to

Fig. 65. A grass topper, adjustable to different heights and essential for managing weeds such as nettles and thistles.

6.5 cm in the early part of the season, and even shorter (about 2.5 cm) later on.

But should grass be at its highest productivity? For horses which tend to obesity it may be preferable to allow grass to grow without cutting, since grass becomes higher in fibre as it matures and lower in available energy. Remember that the horse will be able to eat more in these circumstances so grazing may still need to be restricted.

Nonetheless it is good practice to cut any uneaten vegetation – mainly weeds and the growth on latrines – at least once a year and perhaps up to six times a year. Topping is an important method for controlling weeds, and a

pasture with annual weeds, thistles, nettles or docks should be cut just before these plants flower, so that they cannot seed. Constant cutting weakens weeds but encourages grasses: it may also weaken wildflowers, so if you have many flower species in your pastures you should not cut the whole sward too frequently in a year, and generally not until late summer so wildflowers have a chance to flower and seed. Note that the topper (fig. 65) should generally be set just above the height of the grazed grass, as the idea is not to mow all the vegetation but just the plants whose growth is unchecked by grazing.

When grass is cut and left to lie, there is a mulching effect: that is, it returns nutrients to the soil. If large amounts of grass cuttings are left undisturbed, the nutrient effect can be too high and encourage the growth of weeds. It can also smother less dominant plants and even create patches of bare ground. **Most important:** if cuttings form a thick pile they ferment, and if horses are able to eat such cuttings they can get colic. This is one reason why the topper should be set high; additionally it is important to manage the cuttings by topping frequently enough to prevent an accumulation of cut material. Horses will safely eat cut material which has been spread about, including wilted thistles and nettles which will give them beneficial minerals. Removing cut material from overgrown patches, particularly latrines, and spreading it on to shorter grazed areas (with a harrow or raking by hand) will help to even out the return of nutrients to the soil thus preventing lush growth. If there is any doubt about the safety of cuttings, either they must be picked up and removed – by hand,

Fig. 66. A baling machine can be useful not only for baling hay but in cases where paddock toppings threaten to smother the vegetation. If weeds are collected be sure to clean the baler thoroughly before making hay.

Fig. 67. Ragwort must be removed before fields are cut, and preferably as soon as it appears. The best method of removal is by hand.

by harrowing and collecting, or with a baling machine (fig. 66) – or the horses must be moved from the field until the cuttings have rotted down completely. This is particularly true if there is any chance of ragwort (fig. 67) having been cut; **remember that ragwort should be pulled up and destroyed before any cutting takes place** (*see Chapter 4*).

RESTING

Grass needs to be rested periodically to recover from being grazed and to keep the balance of grasses, legumes, weeds and wildflowers. Because horses are grazed in restricted areas, the best patches of grass are constantly grazed, and if they are overgrazed the vegetation will gradually be weakened and may eventually die. Removing horses from paddocks for even a few weeks enables the grass to grow again and send out new tillers, as long as its growth point has not been damaged (*see Chapter 2*). If manure and cut vegetation have been harrowed they will rot down and provide the grass with extra nutrients in a natural manner. Even in winter there will be some recovery if the grass is rested in this way.

One way of resting grass is by strip grazing (fig. 68). Here one end of a larger field is made available for grazing, and the front temporary fence (electric fencing is ideal) is moved forward

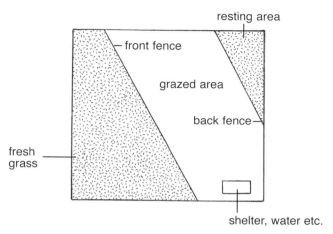

Fig. 68. Strip grazing, with two temporary fences moved across the field. Ensure that water sources and shelter are always available.

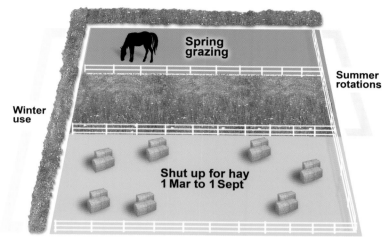

Fig. 69. Paddock rotations are particularly valuable when grazing is limited, to avoid damage to the sward.

daily or weekly to allow a little fresh grass, while a back fence is similarly moved to allow the grazed grass to rest. This method is sometimes used to restrict the intake of ponies, but in fact it ensures that the best grass is available and is better for horses needing good productive grass.

In other circumstances the area available for grazing should be in at least two paddocks and preferably three. Where there is a need to maximise grass growth, each paddock can be grazed for a few weeks and rested for a few weeks in rotation during the main growing season from about April to October.

Assuming that there are three areas available for grazing, the way they are used should be adjusted to the season, the state of the grass and the condition (e.g. fat or lean) of the grazing animals. In spring, for example, one or even two paddocks could be shut up for hay while the

third paddock is grazed (fig. 69). Once hay is taken, the grazed paddock could be rested while the other two are grazed. For most of the winter, all three paddocks can be grazed simultaneously, with the possibility of shutting up any one of them to recover if it becomes wet or damaged. For maximum growth on limited grazing, follow a régime of three weeks' grazing and six weeks' rest for each paddock during the growing season, and graze two or all three over winter.

It is not a good idea to graze the same paddock at the same time every year, as plants are sensitive to the timing of grazing. If, for example, the same grasses are always grazed in May, some will become dominant and others may die out. To keep a good range of plant species, it is best to vary the timing of grazing. There are two exceptions to this: (1) if you purposely want to increase or decrease a particular plant species

Fig. 70. One horse per compartment is not ideal for the horse or for the grass (but note how the white electric rope used in the foreground fits into the landscape much better than the white tape and posts used elsewhere).

Fig. 71. Horses in company, with plenty of space and natural features.

(for example, white clover), grazing at the same time of year for a few years may be necessary; (2) if you have a traditional hayfield with a range of wildflowers, this should be managed as it always has been, which is likely to be cutting for hay and grazing afterwards.

The size of each paddock needs to be big enough to accommodate the number of horses comfortably. Ideally this should be between 0.3 and 0.4 hectare (3/4 to 1 acre) in each paddock for each full-sized (500 kg) horse. It is quite common nowadays, particularly in livery yards, to have small compartments ('turn-out' areas) for each horse divided from others by an electric fence, or to manage rotations by dividing already small paddocks into two or three (fig. 70). However, this is not always the best approach for the grass and is particularly uncomfortable for the horse. Horses like to have company, and being on their own in a field surrounded by electric tape – so that they cannot even talk over the fence, let alone scratch or rest their chins – is very frustrating for them. Even if they can see other horses they will be less satisfied than if they can touch them and stand nose to tail. They also need room to run and play, and where electric fence is used they should not feel anxious all the time about the possibility of touching it, but should have enough space in which to relax (fig. 71). They will not get sufficient exercise in a small area, but will tend to stay in the same spot. Five horses in a two-hectare (five-acre) field with hedges and trees on at least some boundaries will be happier and safer than five horses in half-acre or even acre plots surrounded by electric tape. As long as they are not fed in the field (and this includes being caught with polo mints!) there should be less jealousy and thus a reduced chance of kicking and biting. Some horses are natural bullies, and these may need to be kept in different conditions, perhaps with just one subservient companion. But there is even more reason for such horses to be kept in large areas where they will not feel a need to protect their own space.

Over-small compartments also tend to lead to poor grass. On small paddocks it is essential to pick up the droppings, with the result that the whole area is often grazed very short – and even if a second field is available, rotations are not frequent enough to avoid permanent damage to the grass. In these circumstances it may be better to have one large field and dispense with the rotations. Basically this means that there will not be enough land available for the horses to graze all year, and they will need to be kept stabled for longer or alternative arrangements made.

A new idea particularly for horses and ponies which tend to be overweight is to fence off the centre of the field, leaving a wide track around the edge for the horses (fig. 72). This mirrors the circumstances of the wild horse and encourages horses to keep moving around the track, particularly if items such as mineral licks, water troughs and shelter are available at widely spaced points. The track can follow a varied route

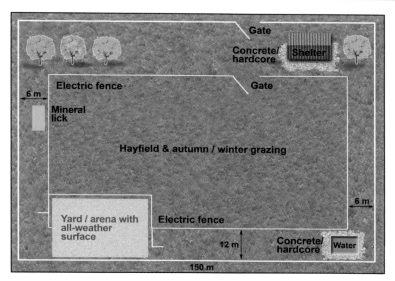

Fig. 72. The new 'paddock paradise' concept, where horses are restricted to the outside track during the growing season, encouraging them to move more and eat less.

for added length or interest. It can be a good way of limiting summer grass while the centre parts of the field are rested and then made available for the winter, but may not work on fields prone to waterlogging and mud.

It is difficult to determine the area required per horse, but as a rule of thumb it is safer to start with a total of one hectare (2.5 acres) per full-sized, 500 kg horse divided into two or three paddocks rather than to assume that you can manage with just one acre. There are many variables which govern how much land you need, which are discussed in Chapter 5. However, the majority of problems associated with the condition of horse-grazed grass are caused by too many horses on not enough land.

CHAPTER 4

PROBLEMS FOR PONIES AND GRASS

THE MOST DIFFICULT ISSUES

Although being at grass is the most natural place for horses and ponies, and is where they most like to be, the unnatural paddock situations in which they are kept present us with a number of particular problems. Specific situations can cause injury or illness, and in some circumstances even death, if they are not managed correctly. The following are the main problems to be addressed.

LAMINITIS, OBESITY AND EQUINE METABOLIC SYNDROME

The disease which causes the most problems for equine animals at grass, particularly ponies, is laminitis. There are a number of causes (not necessarily connected to diet), but the most frequent, and the one considered here, is presumed to be the intake of excess carbohydrate from lush, rapidly growing or fertilised grass. Often a pony (or quite possibly a horse) is obese from too high an intake of sugars and starch, which can lead to its own problems of equine metabolic syndrome (insulin resistance). As over-eating foods high in energy is one of the underlying causes of laminitis, obesity and equine metabolic syndrome, they are dealt with together here.

There has been an increase in obesity (as many as one-third of horses are overweight) which is now seen as the most serious welfare issue in equine animals. It is linked not only with laminitis and metabolic syndrome but with joint conditions (including arthritis), heat stress and breathing problems. Obesity is defined by body condition scoring, and a horse is considered obese if the ribs are difficult to feel, if there is a crease along the spine, if there is a large neck crest and fat around the top of the tail, and fat deposits on the inner thigh, shoulder blades, rump and withers.

Three management factors combine to cause obesity: (1) lack of exercise – some horses seem to be kept more as pets than as animals to ride and work; (2) overfeeding of cereals and other feeds of high calorific value 'out of the bag' – animals in light work need nothing other than forage (hay, grass, etc.) feeds; (3) the increase of high-sugar varieties of ryegrass and the use of fertiliser on horse-grazed pastures.

Obese horses (fig. 73) may develop equine metabolic syndrome, which means that they have high insulin and glucose levels. Metabolic syndrome is often accompanied by increased thirst and urination, infertility in mares, and laminitis. It can be treated by restricting the diet and increasing the levels of exercise. It is important to devise a method of allowing horses to have unrestricted movement at pasture while keeping their intake levels low, for example by fitting a grazing muzzle.

Laminitis is the inflammation of the sensitive fleshy laminae within the feet, which leads to extreme pain, as because of the hard hoof wall there is nowhere for the swelling to go. It can lead to changes in the structure of the foot (fig. 74) which cause permanent lameness, and the pony may have to be put down as a result. Unfortunately laminitis is quite common: cases are increasing and it has been estimated that every year 7% of the equine population in Britain suffers from the acute form (i.e. an attack of lameness; the chronic form is when there have been changes to the structure of the foot).

Grass contains a number of nutrients, including carbohydrates, proteins, fat, vitamins and minerals. Carbohydrates come in two forms: simple, such as sugars and starch, and complex, such as cellulose and lignin (both forms of fibre). Horses cannot break down starch satisfactorily. Cereals such as oats and barley are high in it, and an excess of these is known to cause laminitis. Grass is not particularly high in starch (though seed heads contain some), but can contain high

Fig. 73. An obese horse, with large crest and fat deposits on shoulders, withers and rump. This horse is also in the early stages of laminitis, showing the tell-tale stance with weight on the hind legs – note also the depression in the grass where he has been lying down.

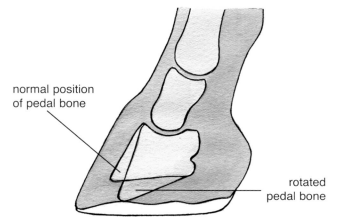

normal position of pedal bone

rotated pedal bone

Fig. 74. The structure of the foot is altered in cases of chronic laminitis.

Fig. 75. Native ponies in their natural surroundings must cover great distances to obtain sufficient nutrition from the high fibre, low fertility vegetation that surrounds them. The combination of correct diet and exercise avoids metabolic problems.

levels of water-soluble carbohydrates – sugars and fructans – which also cause laminitis. Cereals and lush grass are the main diet-related causes of laminitis, but scientists are still unsure of exactly how it occurs.

In order to avoid laminitis it is important for ponies and horses to be fed high fibre food which is low in water-soluble carbohydrates. Native ponies in their natural surroundings live on generally infertile soils where there is a plenty of diverse vegetation, and to find enough suitable vegetation to make up their diet they have to cover considerable distances (fig. 75). This combination of exercise, fibre and low fertility keeps them healthy and prevents laminitis. We must try to provide these same conditions in much smaller and enclosed spaces.

It is important for animals of the type prone to obesity and laminitis to have suitable vegetation in their pastures: i.e. a range of grasses and flowers. The worst pasture for them is an agricultural type of ryegrass and white clover, and worse still is the use of artificial nitrogen fertiliser.

Since the 18th century, ryegrass has been the cheapest and most common grass seed on the market: specifically bred to provide food high in protein and water-soluble carbohydrates for cattle and sheep, for fattening and producing milk, and low in fibre for easier digestibility by ruminant animals. As described in Chapter 1, horses must have a high fibre diet, low in sugar and starch, and they do not need high levels of protein.

Different strains or 'varieties' of ryegrass have been bred to produce flower-heads at different times over the growing season – early, intermediate and late – so as to lengthen the grazing season and ensure good quality grass throughout. Ryegrass cultivars (bred varieties) are either *diploid* or *tetraploid* (referring to the number of sets of chromosomes). Tetraploid varieties are generally higher in sugar than diploid, and as they have a tall and upright growth habit are less likely to form the kind of ground-covering turf that is best for horses. Tetraploids were originally sold as not suitable for horses because of their sugar content, but this warning seems to have been forgotten. More recently a number of strains of diploid ryegrass known as 'High Sugar' varieties have been introduced. The higher level of sugars enables sheep and cattle to utilise the available protein more efficiently. The High Sugar grasses can contain half as much sugar again as even the tetraploid ryegrasses, which

PADDOCK GRAZING MIX

Simple System Ltd Paddock Grazing Mix is a ryegrass free blend of grass species and varieties which are higher in fibre and lower in digestible nutrients such as sugars.

It includes a combination of hardy and creeping species best suited to keeping your sward intact and repairing the turf after heavy use.
These more traditional species are a little more expensive but are more suitable for equines than the more highly "improved" species and varieties used in modern agriculture.

In addition we have added a legume for its mineral rich content and its soil improvement characteristics but it is also known to be safe for horses.

The mix contains the following species:

Timothy
Meadow fescue
Creeping red fescue
Smooth stalked meadow
   grass
Birdsfoot trefoil

The mix may vary slightly in varieties according to the availability of these scarcer species.

Natural Pony Paddock

We recommend the use of a non-ryegrass mixture for ponies and horses which require less protein rich swards. **The following mixture is designed to provide a maintenance diet for animals that are not working hard.**
Use this mixture for ponies with a tendency to become overweight or those prone to laminitis. This type of mixture is slower to establish than those with ryegrass but the resulting turf is dense and more resilient. Traditional herbs are included as standard. This mixture should be sown no later than mid September.

3.00 kg certified COSMOLIT
          meadow fescue
1.50 kg certified BARCEL or
          similar tall fescue
1.50 kg certified SPARTA cocksfoot
2.50 kg certified CORAIL creeping
          red fescue
1.00 kg certified BORNITO sheeps fescue
1.00 kg certified PROMESSE timothy
0.50 kg certified TENO smaller catstail
1.00 kg certified EVORA smooth
          meadowgrass
1.00 kg certified DASAS rough stalked
          meadowgrass
0.50 kg certified HIGHLAND browntop
0.10 kg commercial meadow foxtail
0.10 kg commercial sweet vernal grass
0.80 kg commercial crested dogstail
0.25 kg burnet
0.10 kg ribgrass
0.05 kg yarrow
0.10 kg sheeps parsley

Fig. 76. Some companies produce ryegrass-free seed mixes with a few wildflowers included, which will be suitable for both horses and ponies. Because they are slower growing and less productive sufficient land must be provided.

already contain between two and four times as much as the native grasses normally eaten by ponies. Unfortunately there has been no warning about the effect of High Sugar grasses on horses and these varieties are sometimes included in off-the-shelf seed mixes for horse pastures. Check carefully before buying grass seed (fig. 76).

Ryegrass has been described as the Darth Vader of grasslands. This is because if it is growing in fertile conditions – particularly if artificial nitrogen fertiliser is applied – it will take over and suppress other plants. The final outcome is a large amount of productive grass, all of one species, high in protein and energy and low in fibre. Feeding this to horses is like feeding them junk food such as burgers and fizzy drinks. They become not only obese but also addicted to sugars, greedily eating more and more of the readily available food until their intake is as much as 7% of their body-weight instead of the recommended 2.5%. Greediness is noticeable in horses which develop equine metabolic syndrome, but once they are changed from a sugar-rich diet they return to normal eating habits.

Ryegrass is particularly productive if nitrogen fertiliser is applied, so this must be avoided; in fact even if a pasture contains a variety of grasses, especially if it has wildflowers as well, inorganic fertiliser should never be applied. A diverse sward can be altered in just a few years by constant applications of nitrogen fertiliser, until the range of grasses and flowers – which is just what horses want – becomes a species-poor sward, probably dominated by ryegrass. It is vital for pasture grazed by laminitics not to be fertilised. Inorganic nitrogen fertiliser in particular must not be used, and if an occasional boost is required, well-rotted farmyard or stable manure should be applied every few years and a hay cut taken before grazing is resumed.

White clover and other leguminous plants (red clover, trefoils and vetches) have a fertilising effect, as they are able to capture nitrogen from the atmosphere and use it both for their own growth and to supplement the growth of the plants around them. But though this is a slower, more natural release of nutrients than is provided by inorganic fertiliser, white clover has more sugar and starch and less fibre than is suitable for most horses. Where laminitis is a real problem, clover and High Sugar ryegrasses should be eliminated. If necessary, fields should be re-seeded (but not ploughed up, which will just add to the problem) with slower growing, low-sugar grasses. Timothy has been found to be a good grass for laminitics; other wild British grasses such as red fescue, crested dogstail, rough and smooth meadow grass and common and creeping bent are also suitable. Chapter 3 mentioned ways of introducing different grasses into an existing sward.

The aim when managing horses prone to laminitis must be to reduce the intake of grass rich in water-soluble carbohydrates. If the current pasture vegetation is unsuitable (e.g. too much ryegrass) there are three options, all of which have their own problems. (1) Fit a grazing muzzle (fig. 77), which can reduce grass intake by 50-75%. This is by far the best solution, but some horses are adept at removing muzzles, though there are now some very good designs on the market. (2) Only allow short periods of grazing – but it has been shown that horses which are grazed for short periods can eat much more in the time allowed to them, so they must be fed with high fibre forage beforehand. (3) It is often recommended to keep the horse on a starvation paddock, but this is not sound. The shortest, freshest grass is the sweetest and most productive, so though it may look as if the paddock is bare there is more inside the horse than you may suppose; it may not be enough to cause laminitis but it may be giving the horse a diet too high in carbohydrates and low in fibre. If the paddock is grazed bare it will certainly cause problems for the vegetation.

If vegetation is incorrect and a grazing muzzle cannot be used, it is preferable to keep the horse on a bark or straw surface (fig. 78) and feed high fibre forage such as lucerne (alfalfa), late season hay or good quality oat straw, and perhaps allow short periods at pasture immediately after feeding one of these forages. It must be ensured that the horse receives sufficient high fibre food to keep him healthy, keep the digestive system working and avoid stomach ulcers, colic or hyperlipaemia.

A recommendation often made is to keep laminitics and horses with equine metabolic syndrome or prone to obesity off grass altogether. This may sometimes be the safest option, but it is certainly not a good long-term outlook for the horse, which is happiest when at grass. If native ponies can roam freely on their many acres of grassland without dietary problems there must be a way of allowing them to graze safely at pasture. Except in the case of the most naturally fertile soil (e.g. some clays or riverside meadows), it is possible to sow a grass mix which contains a wide variety of low-sugar, high fibre plants, some of which the horse may not find palatable, so he

Fig. 77. A well-fitted grazing muzzle can be the solution to many grazing worries.

Fig. 78. A bark surface allows sufficient exercise, and if high fibre forage is fed in addition this is a superior alternative to a starvation paddock.

will have to spend longer searching for the food he requires. The idea of a track around the perimeter of the field mentioned in Chapter 3 could also help. This may mean that more land is necessary to provide sufficient grazing, with the advantage that animals are able to get more exercise as they graze. For very susceptible ponies a grazing muzzle may still be a requirement.

GRASS SICKNESS

Grass sickness is a very unpleasant and debilitating disease affecting as many as 1 in 200 horses and usually resulting in the horse having to be put down. Symptoms include muscle tremor, salivation and difficulty swallowing, or in its less acute form colic and loss of weight. Unfortunately its cause is still unclear, but it is thought to be due to soil-borne bacteria, and it sometimes occurs repeatedly in the same field. Where it is found, some suggestions have been put forward as to how to manage the field in order to minimise the chance of the disease recurring.

- Avoid disturbing the soil, in particular by poaching, overgrazing or heavy harrowing.
- Do not use nitrogen or any compound fertilisers (organic or inorganic) high in nitrogen.
- Eradicate white clover, which may be a trigger factor.
- Avoid grazing in cold dry weather in spring and early summer where there are several consecutive days of a temperature between 7 and 11 °C.
- Top the grass regularly.
- Graze other species (sheep, cattle) on the same field.
- Feed hay or haylage in addition to grazing.

These guidelines are similar to those often put forward for laminitics, and in general represent sensible rules for pasture management for all horses.

WINTER TURN-OUT AND POACHING

If horses and ponies are able to spend time at pasture every day of the year they are happier and healthier and often more pleasant to ride. When they are not in full work, allowing them to be out for at least a few hours a day can be of vital importance, and ponies, youngstock, broodmares and resting horses ideally should be out 24 hours a day with suitable food and shelter.

Not all pastures can stand up to this use over the winter. Clay soils can be particularly difficult, quickly becoming waterlogged and muddy in wet weather. If vegetation is sparse at the beginning of winter, overgrazing can easily occur, and bare ground and mud will follow. If enough land is allowed for each horse, it is possible to shut some paddocks up so that they can benefit from the surge of autumn growth – perhaps after a hay cut – and begin winter with a good thick cover of vegetation. This will do more than anything to prevent ground being damaged during bad weather.

Where drainage is good, horses should be given free range of all the land available from about November to March, depending on weather conditions. At this time grass growth is depressed, but as long as the sward is not damaged there will be minimal effect on the capacity of the grass to recover once the growing season starts. When grass growth begins in earnest, the horses can be confined to a smaller area as explained in Chapter 3.

Fig. 79. A sacrifice paddock which has been in use all winter is still nothing but mud in the spring. The vegetation which grows back will be mainly weeds and annual grasses.

Fig. 80. Ridge and furrow grassland is of historical importance, representing agricultural methods from hundreds of years ago. This feature and wild flowers (such as early purple orchid) can be damaged by overuse during wet winter conditions.

Where drainage is a problem, consideration can be given to improving it (*see Chapter 2*). However, it is more likely that daily turnout may have to be curtailed in order to protect the ground. It may be that horses can only be turned out to grass for a few hours a day, or perhaps not at all on especially wet days. Although as much land as possible should be available for winter use, in poor conditions it is wise to use a flexible rotation of fields. Even in the period of depressed grass growth, if there is minor damage to the sward on one day it will recover if the horses are immediately removed from that paddock and another is used.

To save horses from having to stand in the stable for long periods – particularly if they are not in heavy work – and also to allow them to spend sufficient time foraging and taking in high fibre food, alternatives can be found. The use of a 'sacrifice paddock', which is grazed to destruction and is re-seeded in the spring, is not recommended (fig. 79). If it is on a slope or in an area where wind erosion is a problem, soil may wash or blow away, entering adjacent ditches or watercourses. Here soil will not only clog the ditch, but will take with it nutrients such as phosphorus which will cause increased vegetation growth in the ditch or watercourse and have a detrimental effect on water quality. Any botanical interest in the pasture – species-richness or unusual species such as orchids – will be ruined, and even archaeological features such as ridge and furrow (fig. 80) can be damaged.

However, giving the horse the opportunity to move freely and run if he wishes is not only good exercise but excellent for mental well-being. If a

Fig. 81. Even a small yard will give the horse some opportunity to move around and avoid boredom; here the arrangement allows him to have access to both the arena and the paddock. When the paddock is in use, leaving the gate open and feeding in the yard will help to avoid poaching in gateways and feeding areas.

Fig. 82. A combination of gateways and an over-flowing water tank has led to an un-pleasant mess. Drainage beneath the gateway, a free-draining surface material and concrete beneath the tank will help to prevent this.

well-drained, well-vegetated paddock is not available, an arena or yard can also be a good turnout solution, whether indoors or out (fig. 81). A properly constructed all-weather surface is not necessary, as a layer of bark or even straw can be used. Avoid a waterlogged or muddy yard, which has obvious health implications, leading to diseases such as thrush and mud fever. High fibre forage can be provided at various points around the yard, encouraging the horse to move around, and extending the time he spends eating. Studies have shown that supplying different kinds of forage –

hay, alfalfa chop, haylage etc. – increases beneficial nutrients, but remember to introduce new feeds gradually and to feed a consistent diet.

Gateways and the surroundings of water troughs and field shelters are often areas which turn to mud, even if the rest of the field remains in good condition (fig. 82). There are a number of ways of managing these areas. Drainage can be improved by digging out the soil and filling with hardcore or medium-sized gravel. However, horses do not enjoy standing on such surfaces, and will simply stand beside them and increase

Fig. 83. Plastic mesh specially manufactured for use in areas of hard wear can help to avoid vegetation loss if correctly laid.

the area of mud. A covering of bark, crag (crushed shells) or even re-seeded soil will solve this problem. Another solution is to use specially manufactured plastic grids or matting, which if laid on an even surface can be very effective (fig. 83). Grass seed is sown through them immediately after laying, and the growing grass forms a tight layer which both covers the plastic and helps to hold it in place, while the plastic protects the grass roots. Horses should not be turned out where these materials are in use until a good covering of grass is present, as the surface can be slippery.

WEEDS AND POISONOUS PLANTS

Weeds are defined as plants growing where they are not wanted. To a farmer trying to grow productive grass for cattle, any flowers in the grassland are 'weeds', except for certain clovers. This is because flowers have a lower sugar content than the grasses they replace. But to the horse owner certain flowers are acceptable and 'weeds' are generally those plants which tend to take over a pasture and which will not be eaten by the horse, or those which are poisonous to varying degrees if the horse does eat them.

As was noted in Chapter 2 there are a number of species which can quickly become established when ground has been disturbed, either because they are annual plants with efficient means of producing and spreading seed, or because their seeds persist in the seed bank. These are the plants of gateways and poached areas, such as fat hen, pineappleweed, shepherd's purse and knotgrass (fig. 84). One of the most persistent and difficult plants to appear in this way are docks, which together with thistles and ragwort are classed as 'injurious weeds' and are subject to regulation. The Injurious Weeds Act of 1959 identifies five weed species which must be controlled from spreading on to neighbouring land. These are broad-leaved dock, curled dock, creeping thistle, spear thistle and ragwort. The Ragwort Control Act of 2003 goes further and requires positive action if ragwort is presenting a high risk to horses and other livestock. Every horse owner should be able to identify ragwort, and should remove it immediately from grazed pasture and in particular from hayfields. While growing, ragwort has a bitter taste and horses generally will not touch it. However, when it begins to wilt after being cut or damaged the bitterness goes, but the toxic qualities remain, which is when it becomes dangerous, especially in hay. Ragwort contains a poison which attacks the liver, and its effect is cumulative, so if the

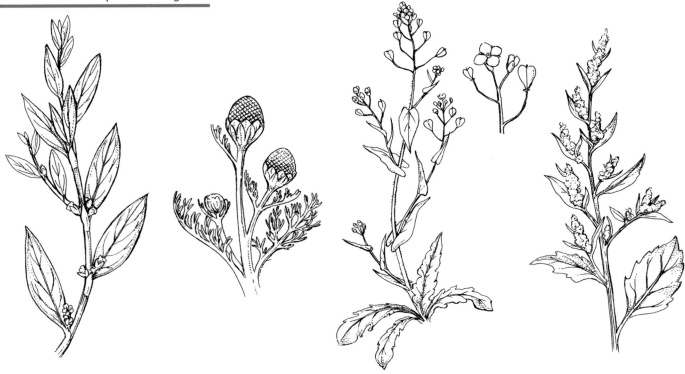

Fig. 84. Weeds typical of gateways: (from left to right) knotgrass (with small pink or white flowers); pineappleweed (yellow flower-heads and feathery leaves, smelling of pineapple); shepherd's purse (tiny white flowers and triangular seed pod); fat hen (insignificant green flowers).

horse eats small amounts over a long period it is just as bad as eating a large amount in a short time. Ponies and horses need only eat 4-8% of their bodyweight in their lifetime for ragwort to kill them – the equivalent of approximately half a bale of hay for a pony and a whole bale for a large horse. *It is a weed which needs to be taken seriously.*

The best way to get rid of ragwort is to dig it up in the spring when the ground is slightly moist and the roots come up easily. If the roots are cut or parts of them left behind, the plant can regenerate. Gloves should always be worn when handling ragwort, as the poison is said to act through the skin. **It must be removed entirely from the pasture and destroyed – preferably by burning – so that horses have no access to the dying plant.**

Large infestations of ragwort can be sprayed, though great care must be taken not to kill other beneficial plants, including hedgerow plants, and not to contaminate water sources. In addition, all traces of ragwort must either have rotted away or be removed once the spray has done its job, as

Fig. 85. Ragwort must be removed from horse pastures and particularly from hayfields. Cutting or spraying is less satisfactory than removing by hand, as any part of the plant which remains is poisonous.

Fig. 86. Marsh ragwort (above), found in damp areas; groundsel (above right), found in disturbed areas. Both are members of the ragwort family and are poisonous.

even when dead the plant is still poisonous. Stock cannot be re-introduced to the pasture until it has completely disappeared. An alternative to chemical sprays is citronella oil, which has proved effective and fast-acting. It is only available for spot treatment, as it will scorch grass and other plants if it touches them. It can be used at any time of year and stock may be returned to the pasture in as little as two weeks, as opposed to four to six weeks for conventional herbicides.

All the above refers to the species known as *common ragwort*, or to give it its Latin name *Senecio jacobaea* (fig. 85). However, there are a number of different species, all of which are poisonous to some degree. Oxford ragwort, hoary ragwort, marsh ragwort and groundsel are among the most common (fig. 86).

The two species of thistle which are classed as injurious weeds are included in the Act because of their tendency to spread and take up space which would be better used by grass and other plants. However, they are no danger to horses and when cut and wilted they will be eaten happily by horses and will provide them with minerals and other nutrients.

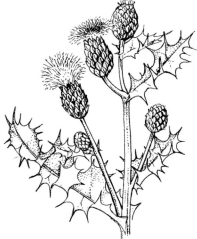

Fig. 87. Creeping thistle spreads easily in overgrazed or disturbed grassland, and can soon take over large areas.

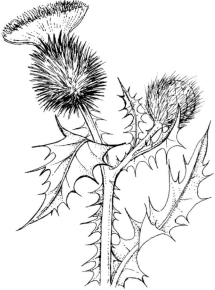

Fig. 88. Spear thistle is easier to control by cutting, but the timing must be right.

Creeping thistle (fig. 87) is a particular problem in horse pastures, as it loves the nutrients of latrine areas and is quick to establish in disturbed, over-grazed patches. Although it produces seed which can travel a long way on the wind as thistle-down, only a small percentage of the seeds are viable, and its main way of spreading is via its roots. Any disturbance of the root system will encourage it to spread. In order to control it, it must be cut frequently over two or three years. The first cut is best made just as the flower-head is showing colour; this will eventually weaken the root system and kill off the plant. If it is cut in its non-flowering stage it will simply produce more stems. Creeping thistles respond to spraying, but spray should not be used if there is a danger to other beneficial plants.

Spear thistle (fig. 88), a much larger thistle with spiny leaves, grows as a solitary plant rather than in large clumps. It is a biennial, so each individual plant dies after two years and as a result produces much larger quantities of viable seed; however, the seed probably only travels a few metres. To control spear thistle it must be cut just before seeding; if it is cut too early it will attempt to flower again. It is quite difficult to kill it by spraying, as the hairs on its leaves tend to keep the spray from reaching its target.

There are several other species of thistle, but in general they do not present problems in horse pasture and indeed may be rare plants which should not be destroyed. The two problem species are easy to identify: *spear thistle* is one of the largest and most readily recognisable, with downy hairs on the large leaves and spines up

Fig. 89. Bristly ox-tongue will grow on disturbed and poorly managed pastures, but will not persist under regular cutting and controlled grazing.

the stem. *Creeping thistle* is one of the few thistle species with a spineless stem; it is also hairless (or with just a few hairs on the underside of the leaves), unlike the majority of other species. Horse owners sometimes object to thistle-like plants with yellow flowers, such as bristly ox-tongue (fig. 89), but they are usually a sign that the pasture soil has been disturbed by over-grazing or over-use in wet weather, and they will not persist if proper management is undertaken.

There are also several species of docks, but only two – *broadleaved dock* (fig. 90) and *curled dock* – are classed as injurious. They can be a

Fig. 90. Patches of broad-leaved dock can be difficult to control and may need constant cutting, targeted spraying or digging out.

Fig. 91. Nettle patches spreading from latrine areas create the best conditions for more nettles to grow; they must be cut and removed, and new seeds may need to be sown.

significant nuisance, particularly where pasture is badly poached over the winter. They produce thousands of seeds over several months each season, and the seed can live in the seed bank for anything from 30 to 80 years! The plant itself is very persistent: if roots are disturbed or cut, they will regenerate, even if lying on the surface of the ground. Therefore if docks are dug up, roots must be removed to about 20 cm below ground and the plants must be disposed of, not left to lie on the pasture. Any cultivations such as ploughing or even heavy harrowing will simply distribute the root segments, each of which can produce a new plant. Cutting will prevent seeding, but the plant will just send up another stem to seed again. Even spraying is often not very effective, and a mixture of treatments may have to be used.

The best defence against docks is to prevent them establishing, by avoiding poaching in the winter and keeping a good dense sward at all times.

A number of other weeds can present problems in horse pastures, but they are not listed as injurious. *Nettles* are often found with creeping thistle in large clumps on latrine areas (fig. 91). Nettles will tend to crowd out any other plant, and there will be just bare ground below their leaves. They like the phosphorus in dung and draw it up into their leaves; when the plant dies the phosphorus goes back into the ground. If a large patch of nettles is being cut it is important to remove all the cuttings from the patch and if necessary re-seed the area, otherwise nettles will simply grow up again in the same place. Like thistles, the wilted nettles are palatable to horses

Fig. 92. Buttercups commonly found in pasture: (top left) creeping buttercup (long stalk on end lobe of leaf); (centre) meadow buttercup (no stalk on end lobe of leaf); (bottom left) bulbous buttercup (turned back sepals under flower-head, furrow down stalk). Celery-leaved buttercup (top right) and lesser spearwort (bottom right) are found in damp places. Buttercups are an irritant and can cause allergies and photosensitivity.

and give them plenty of vitamins and minerals. Because they spread by their roots, they will be weakened by constant cutting, starting as early as possible in the spring. If they are sprayed, the dead nettles must still be removed from the patch and horses should not be allowed to eat them.

Buttercups (fig. 92) are a species which horse owners are often concerned about because of their toxicity. Horses seldom eat them, however, as they are very bitter, and large amounts are needed to cause problems. There are a number of different species: *celery-leaved buttercup* and *lesser spearwort* grow near water and are the

Fig. 93. A boom sprayer towed behind a tractor should generally not be used, as valuable plants will be killed as well as weed species. A hand-held knapsack sprayer (foreground) or a weedwiper is preferable.

most poisonous, but the three most likely to be found in pastures are *bulbous buttercup* (the first to flower in spring), *meadow buttercup* (the tallest) and *creeping buttercup* (the most common). Once cut and wilted, the bitterness and the toxicity disappear, so in hay there is no problem with these three. However, creeping buttercup can be a nuisance because it spreads easily and can suppress grass growth. It can also be a sign of overgrazing and it tends to proliferate especially on damp ground or soil which is prone to waterlogging (often because it is compacted). It can be harrowed in the spring to remove the rooting runners, but the plants should be gathered up and destroyed to prevent re-rooting. Sprays can be effective, but beware of other valuable plants in the sward. Changing the use of the pasture for a couple of years and taking hay instead of grazing may also alleviate the problem.

The best overall approach to dealing with weeds is to create conditions where they find it difficult to establish themselves and persist. A good thick sward which is never grazed below about 5 cm or subject to poaching, and which is topped and harrowed as necessary (unless it is species-rich, in which case more targeted management may be required), will go a long way towards keeping weeds to a minimum.

Note that if spraying is undertaken the specific plant which is causing problems should be targeted by spot-spraying or weed-wiping (fig. 93). Avoid blanket spraying the whole field, which may kill valuable vegetation. The products used should be chosen carefully and applied according to the instructions on the label. Some

cross-section of stem
with interrupted pith

Fig. 94. Poisonous plants of damp places: (left to right) yellow flag iris, marsh marigold and hard rush.

products can only be used by certified spray operators; preferably all spraying should be carried out by an expert. **Always treat sprays with caution**, and remember that they can damage other vegetation and wildlife, and must be kept away from water. Keep horses away from sprayed material for at least as long as the label instructs, and preferably longer.

Many plants are poisonous to horses, some causing only mild problems and others being fatal, and they are not all listed here. Luckily, apart from ragwort, most pastures are unlikely to contain deadly poisonous plants in the grass itself. However, beware of wet or marshy areas, where plants such as yellow flag iris, hard rush, hemlock, marsh marigold, horsetails and silverweed may grow and are toxic (fig. 94). Hedgerows may also present problems, either because of the bushes themselves – buckthorn and alder buckthorn, holly, privet, spindle – the climbing plants such as white bryony, or plants growing at the foot of hedgerows or on woodland edges – dog's mercury, foxglove, cuckoo pint and bracken (fig. 95).

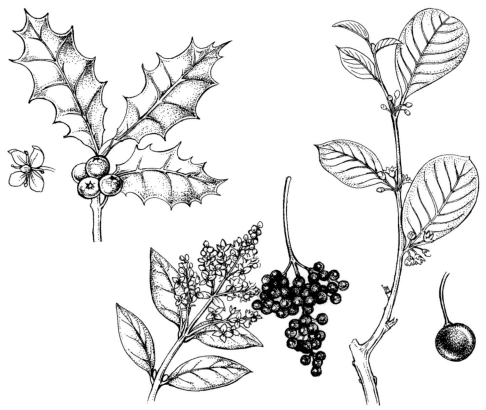

Fig. 95. Poisonous plants of hedgerows and woodlands: (top left) holly, (bottom left) wild privet, (centre) alder buckthorn, (right) dog's mercury.

The most serious hazards come from garden plants, so **where your pasture adjoins a garden be particularly vigilant.** You should be sure that your neighbours do not place any garden cuttings or lawn mowings where horses can reach them. The most dangerous garden plants are box, rhododendron, cherry laurel, laburnum, thuja and robinia (false acacia) (fig. 96). Many flowers which grow from bulbs are poisonous, such as lily of the valley, autumn crocus and bluebells.

From the vegetable garden, potatoes and rhubarb are both toxic. Plants growing in disturbed or waste ground which can cause problems are black and deadly nightshade, thorn apple and poppies (fig. 97).

Three of our native trees must also be noted here. Yews (fig. 98) are highly poisonous. The reason why they are often found in churchyards is that these were once the only places securely fenced from stock where yew trees, valued for

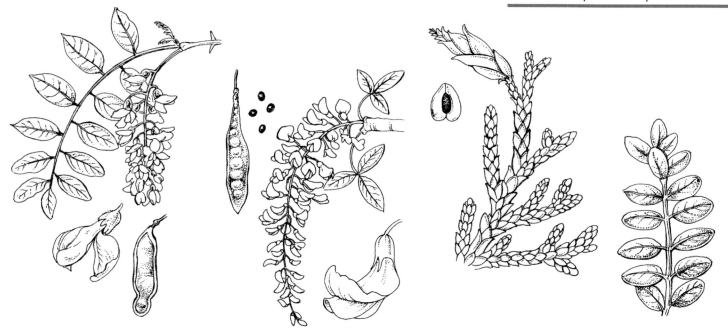

Fig. 96. Poisonous garden trees: (left to right) robinia (white flowers), laburnum (yellow flowers), thuja (evergreen of the cyprus family), box (evergreen).

Fig. 97. Poisonous plants of waste places: (above) black nightshade (white flowers); (right) deadly nightshade.

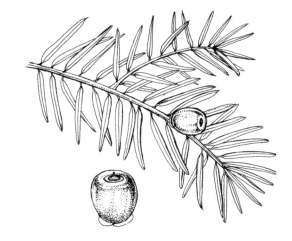

*Fig. 98. Yew tree –
all parts of the tree are deadly poison.*

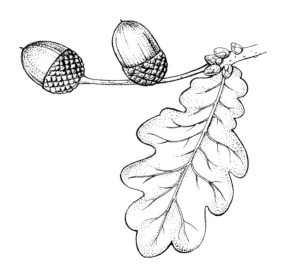

Fig. 99. Oak tree – leaves and acorns can cause digestive problems.

Fig. 100. Beech tree – the triangular nuts or beechmast (above) can cause colic.

their wood, could be safely grown. All parts of the tree are deadly. *Oak trees* (fig. 99) are less of a problem – their leaves and acorns can cause digestive problems if large quantities are eaten, but even then the effects are variable. To be safe it is a good idea to clear up acorns in the autumn when there is less grass available and when they therefore may become attractive to horses. The same is true of *beech trees* (fig. 100), whose nuts (known as beechmast) are palatable to horses and can result in colic, seizures and death.

Luckily, if there is other more attractive food readily available horses are unlikely to eat most poisonous plants. So, again, good grassland management is the key.

WORMS

Horses have a number of internal parasites (worms) which if present in high numbers can cause damage to the gut. They can result in loss of weight, diarrhoea and colic, and in the worst cases can be fatal, especially in young horses.

Internal parasites can be divided into three main categories: *roundworms*, *tapeworms*, and *bots*. Roundworms are the largest group of parasites, and include *large redworms* (also called large strongyle), *small redworms* (small strongyle or cyathostomin), *large roundworms* (ascarids), *pinworms*, and *lungworms* amongst others. All of these spend part of their lives in the horse, but

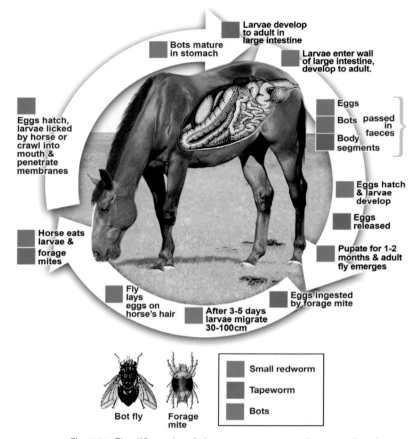

Larvae develop to adult in large intestine

Bots mature in stomach

Larvae enter wall of large intestine, develop to adult.

Eggs

Bots passed in faeces

Body segments

Eggs hatch & larvae develop

Eggs released

Eggs hatch, larvae licked by horse or crawl into mouth & penetrate membranes

Pupate for 1-2 months & adult fly emerges

Horse eats larvae & forage mites

Fly lays eggs on horse's hair

After 3-5 days larvae migrate 30-100cm

Eggs ingested by forage mite

Bot fly   Forage mite

	Small redworm
	Tapeworm
	Bots

Fig. 101. The life cycle of three common parasites: small redworm, tapeworm and bots. They all depend on pasture to complete the cycle.

must complete their life cycle in pasture (fig. 101). They pass out eggs in the horse's droppings, which then hatch on pasture and develop into larvae which the horse may pick up during grazing, and so the cycle begins again.

Large redworm (or large strongyle) is less common than small redworm, as it has been well controlled by wormers, but it is probably the most dangerous internal parasite, damaging the lining of the arteries and the body's vital organs. It is mostly found in young horses.

The *small redworm* (small strongyle) is now the most prevalent parasite in horses. The larvae are picked up by grazing horses, and continue to develop inside them, becoming 'encysted' within the gut wall. Some of them emerge as adults within a few weeks and their eggs are once more passed out with the droppings; others may remain encysted for longer and emerge suddenly in a big group, causing the health problems mentioned above. When the eggs are deposited on the pasture they take three to five days to hatch, and then migrate from the droppings into the pasture. The larvae require moisture, so when conditions are dry they may stay in the moister droppings for several weeks before migrating. Strongyle larvae generally only move up to 30 cm – or at most one metre – from the droppings, and only after there has been sufficient rain.

Large roundworms (ascarids) are mainly a problem in foals, as adult horses develop immunity. Roundworm eggs are particularly durable, and can survive and accumulate in both pastures and stables. This is why it is important to follow good hygiene practices with foals and young horses, and this group is the most vulnerable and most in need of a good worming programme.

Donkeys are the main host for *lungworm*, which is rarely found in horses unless they are

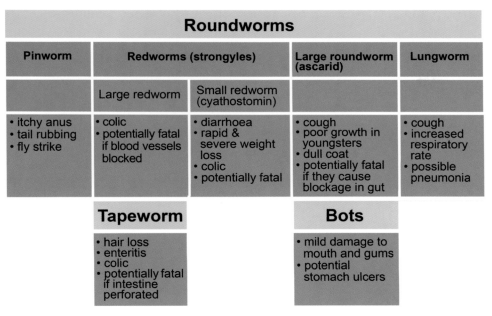

Roundworms				
Pinworm	**Redworms (strongyles)**		**Large roundworm (ascarid)**	**Lungworm**
	Large redworm	Small redworm (cyathostomin)		
• itchy anus • tail rubbing • fly strike	• colic • potentially fatal if blood vessels blocked	• diarrhoea • rapid & severe weight loss • colic • potentially fatal	• cough • poor growth in youngsters • dull coat • potentially fatal if they cause blockage in gut	• cough • increased respiratory rate • possible pneumonia

Tapeworm	Bots
• hair loss • enteritis • colic • potentially fatal if intestine perforated	• mild damage to mouth and gums • potential stomach ulcers

Fig. 102. The main parasite families and the symptoms they can cause.

grazing with donkeys. As its name suggests it settles in the lungs and causes damage there. Horses exhibit a characteristic cough which is not evident in donkeys, so whenever the two are grazed together both should be routinely treated for lungworm.

Pinworms are an irritant rather than a health hazard, laying their eggs around the horse's anus and causing it to rub its tail. Like the other roundworms, the eggs fall on pasture and are taken up by the grazing animal.

The incidence of *tapeworm* infestation has grown since the introduction of and reliance on wormers containing ivermectin, which does not control this parasite. Recently ivermectin products have been combined with other chemicals which will control tapeworms, but in the meantime it has been estimated that two out of three horses are infected. Unlike the roundworm families, the tapeworm requires an intermediate host before its eggs can infect the horse. Segments of tapeworm are passed out with the horse's droppings and release eggs on to the pasture. An insect called a 'forage mite' which lives in pasture and bedding eats the eggs, and is picked up by the horse from grass, hay or straw. The mite tends to be killed off in the pasture by cold weather and frost.

Bots are a type of fly which lays yellow eggs on the horse's coat, frequently on the legs (fig. 103). The horse may lick them off, or the hatched larvae may crawl into the horse's mouth. They then develop in the horse's stomach and are passed out in the dung. They live in the pasture for up to two months before the adult fly emerges.

All these parasites can be controlled by regular worming of the horse with a programme correctly based on the four chemical families in current use. The names of the families, the active ingredients in each family, and some of the products containing these ingredients are given in the table on p. 96. However, there is increasing concern about the overuse of chemicals, particularly when they are used every four to six weeks, as recommended by many manufacturers. There are several reasons for this concern.

• Worms are becoming resistant to the chemicals involved, and there are no wormers currently being developed which use a different chemical family.
• Horses which are frequently wormed lose the tolerance to worms normally acquired in adult life, as they are not given a chance to adjust to a natural low worm burden.
• Constant use of drugs is expensive and not good for the health of the horse.
• Chemicals in the dung have a detrimental effect on the invertebrates which help to break down dung in pasture, and which feed and aerate the soil through this process.
• Chemicals also have a detrimental effect on the invertebrates which eat worm larvae and help to reduce it in pastures.
• Chemicals in the dung have adverse effects on the wider biodiversity, including bats and birds.

The chemical family causing the most problem in all these respects is the one which contains *moxidectin* and *ivermectin*, which have become the most popular ingredients for horse wormers.

To avoid environmental damage, horse owners should restrict the use of chemicals, as other land managers and stock keepers are required to do. Particularly in the face of increased resistance of worms to the known chemical families of wormers, worming should be kept to a minimum; a 4–6 weekly routine dosing should be unnecessary. It is cheaper and more effective to carry out a faecal worm count (fig. 104) once or twice a year (more often if there is cause for concern, such

Fig. 103. Bot worms on a horse's leg.

as new horses coming in or horses losing condition); this will give a good indication of the current worm burden of the horse. The worm count is easily done by sending a sample of fresh dung to one of the several companies which provide this service, and is more informative and less expensive than a monthly worming.

There are a number of ways of controlling parasites in horses, used either with or instead of worming agents, and mainly based on pasture management. The most frequently recommended is picking up droppings. This must be done within three days, before the eggs can hatch, though in the winter it might be possible to leave it a few days longer. There is little point (as far as worm control is concerned) in picking up droppings less often than this, as the larvae may have migrated into the pasture. In fact it can be

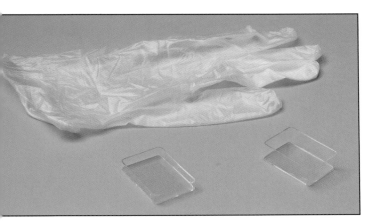

Fig. 104. Taking a sample for a faecal worm count is quick and straightforward using the glove and receptacle supplied by the companies which provide the service.

detrimental, as removing the droppings encourages the horses to graze where they lay, therefore increasing the likelihood of their picking up the larvae. Remember that the formation of latrines is the horse's own method of parasite control. Other advantages and disadvantages of picking up droppings were discussed in Chapter 3.

Harrowing, also mentioned in Chapter 3, is a controversial method of control but can be very effective. If it is carried out after the horses have been removed from the field, the droppings are spread and broken up, causing larvae to die off. If the weather is hot and dry, this will be especially effective, as the droppings will be desiccated and the larvae will have no moisture on which to survive. If it is not possible to remove horses, simply harrowing within the latrine areas will have the same effect, eliminating the risk of spreading larvae on to the grazed areas.

Rotating the grazing and resting the paddocks also helps to diminish the likelihood of the larvae surviving, as they cannot complete their life cycle without the presence of horses. Unfortunately there is no hard evidence as to how long worm larvae can persist in pasture. It depends on weather conditions – they will last longer in warm wet conditions than in hot, dry weather or cold frosty weather – and on the type of parasite. Apparently large roundworm (ascarid) eggs can survive for a number of years, and others may be able to survive over the winter. The main reason for rotating is to prevent a build-up of droppings and parasites and give them a chance to break down and be predated. Horses can be wormed just before being moved on to rested pasture, which will allow a longer period before worming needs to take place again.

The natural breakdown of droppings and predation on larvae by beneficial insects and birds is often overlooked. Dung beetles work on droppings by shredding the dung and taking dung balls into underground chambers where they lay their eggs. In so doing they destroy the habitat for the worm larvae, help the droppings to decompose, and improve soil structure and organic matter. A number of other invertebrates also help in the decomposition of dung, including other beetles, mites, ants, millipedes, spiders, flies and earwigs. Some of these, as well as ladybird and lacewing larvae, are also predatory invertebrates which will attack the worm eggs and larvae themselves and break the life cycle of the horse's parasites. If there is overuse of ivermectin-based wormers, or if droppings are removed, this beneficial action of invertebrates cannot take place.

Where horses are fed with concentrates and some grains pass through into the droppings, birds will scratch around in the dung, taking both seeds and invertebrates. This will help to spread the droppings to good effect, but it may cut down on the number of invertebrates and in particular dung beetles.

Letting sheep and cattle graze before or after horses is a very good way of controlling parasites. Parasitic worms are specific to different types of animal and must pass through the correct host (e.g. horse or cow or donkey) to complete their life cycle. If cattle take up worm eggs and larvae deposited by horses, the life cycle will be broken.

If these management recommendations are followed, then rather than routinely using wormers a regular faecal worm count will safely monitor the horse's worm burden. Worm counts will not identify encysted larvae (those dormant in the gut wall) or tapeworm. Thus an annual treatment against tapeworm (using either *praziquantel* or a double dose of *pyrantel*, the active ingredients) is required, normally in the autumn. If bots have been identified by the yellow eggs on the horse's coat, a dose of *ivermectin* or *moxidectin* can be given over the winter. As all these treatments except praziquantel are also effective against most of the roundworm family,

an adult horse may only require one further treatment in the spring, using *pyrantel*, *fenbendazole* or *mebendazole*. If there is concern about encysted redworms, particularly in young or elderly horses, *moxidectin* or a five-day course of *fenbendazole* can be given at the end of the year.

A combination of faecal worm count and two to three doses of wormer per year should suit adult horses in good condition. Wormers should be alternated as much as possible – using different wormers in different years – to avoid a build-up of resistance. It is important to work from the names of the active ingredients, not the brand name of the product. *Ivermectin* wormers are the most environmentally unfriendly and should be used sparingly, if at all; if they are used it is very important to be aware that ivermectin kills beneficial insects too and renders the droppings sterile so that they are not broken down properly. All droppings should be removed from pasture as soon as possible for two weeks after treatment with ivermectin.

Continuing the use of these products when there is no need for them will cancel out their future effectiveness. Good pasture management and provision of adequate acreage for each horse is the most sustainable way of dealing with worms.

Chemical family	Active ingredients	Typical brands
Macrocylic lactones	moxidectin, ivermectin	Equest, Eqvalan
Pyrimidines	pyrantel	Strongid-P
Benzimidazoles	fenbendazole, mebendazole	Panacur
Isoquinoline pyrazine	praziquantel (tapeworm only)	Equitape

Note: some brands combine active ingredients to treat a range of parasite types.

CHAPTER 5

THE PERFECT PASTURE

A DESCRIPTION OF THE IDEAL AND HOW TO KEEP IT THAT WAY

According to tradition the perfect pasture for horses is a south-facing slope on chalky soil, which provides several of the requirements discussed in this book: a calcareous soil with good levels of calcium in the vegetation; a well-draining soil, as (a) chalk is permeable and (b) the slope precludes standing water; a warm soil, being south-facing, so that natural vegetation growth is maximised and starts early in the season; a typical chalk sward of low fertility and high diversity, perfect for the horse's nutritional needs. It is no accident that the main racehorse breeding areas of Britain are on chalk in Newmarket, Berkshire and Wiltshire (fig. 105).

These conditions are not available to many horse-owners, but grassland can be managed so that it comes as close as possible to the ideal. From the information given in the previous chapters, we can identify a number of simple rules which will enable us to give our horses the best possible pasture:

- *Do* provide enough land.
- *Do not* plough up existing grass.
- *Do not* use artificial nitrogen fertiliser.
- *Do* rest grassland.
- *Do* manage latrines.
- *Do* top weeds and other rank growth.
- *Do* avoid poaching.
- *Do not* overgraze.
- *Do* extend the range of grasses and flowers in the pasture.
- *Do* consider wildlife and the environment.

The calendar on p. 98 also lists the main pasture tasks and their optimum timing.

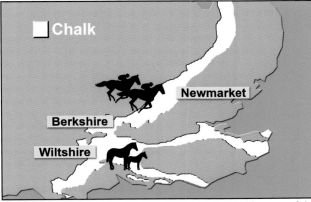

Fig. 105. The outcrop of southern chalk coincides with some of the main racehorse breeding areas such as Newmarket and Lambourn.

January
Cut hedges.
Clear ditches.

February
Apply calcified seaweed to raise pH levels any time between now and September.

March
Grass begins vigorous growth at 6°C.
Spread manure or organic fertiliser if needed, apply lime.
Harrow resting field.
Rest pasture now and in April to reduce white clover.

April
Start topping thistles, docks and nettles, dig out and destroy ragwort.
Shut up fields for hay.
Restrict grazing for next 3 months.
Re-seed bare patches in resting fields.

May
Continue topping weeds and harrowing – or spray (and remove) ragwort, nettles, creeping thistle, docks and bracken.
Rest and rotate pasture if necessary.

June
Graze species-rich grass lightly and allow to flower.
Start making haylage and (mid-June at earliest) hay.
Spray spear thistle, dig up or spray docks, cut bracken repeatedly.

July
Remove and destroy all ragwort before it seeds.
Cut spear thistle before flowering.
Cut rushes repeatedly.
Continue topping, harrowing and resting as necessary.
Best month for hay-making.

August
Spread manure and rest treated fields.
Beware overgrazing droughted grass.
Sow new grass fields or oversow existing ones.
Graze re-growth on hay fields.
Rest pasture to reduce clover.

September
Second spurt of grass growth – beware laminitis.
Shut up fields for winter grazing.
Continue to remove ragwort, cut spear thistle.

October
Grass may still make vigorous growth.
Shut up and top species-rich grass for the winter.

November
Apply lime to low pH grass.
Bring horses off wet pasture.
Shut up fields for hay in next few months.

December
Allow grazing over as large an area as possible in dry weather, or use well-vegetated fields.

PROVIDE ENOUGH LAND

It is difficult to give a hard and fast rule about how many horses a certain area of land should be able to carry, because there are so many variables. If the soil type is clay it will be naturally more fertile as it holds water and nutrients; on the other hand it is more likely to become waterlogged in winter and therefore unusable. Thin and droughty sandy or chalky soils are less productive over the summer but may support a longer grazing period. Parts of the country with higher rainfall will produce more grass than drier areas, but rainfall can also vary over a particular season and affect the growth. The amount of time the horse is at pasture – 24 hours a day all year, or summer nights and a couple of hours in the winter – will obviously make a big difference, as will the type of horse, from Shetland to Shire. If other animals are kept, or hay is taken, more land will be needed. Finally, the time, effort and machinery available for grassland management

Fig. 106. A pasture which gives the horses plenty of space and sufficient grazing will result in happier horses and a better environment.

may also dictate whether or not the pasture reaches its full potential.

To summarise, the options which affect the number of horses on a given amount of land are:

- The size and breed of horses grazing.
- The amount of time horses spend at grass each day and over the year.
- The type and condition of the soil.
- The type of vegetation.
- Whether hay is taken and other livestock grazed.
- The management capability.

One fact is certain, however: the often used figure of one acre (0.4 hectares) per horse is unlikely to be enough. Sometimes the suggestion is two acres (0.8 hectares) for the first horse and one acre thereafter, which is better, but a more appropriate rule of thumb, as mentioned in Chapter 3, is one hectare (2.5 acres) per horse. If you start with this assumption, you can then adjust for the actual circumstances: for example one horse out only during the daytime might only need 0.6 hectares (divided into two when necessary), and a small pony may only need 0.4 hectares altogether.

As horses are happiest when they are out in groups (fig. 106), a field size which equals one acre (0.4 hectares) per horse (so three horses on 3 acres or 1.2 hectares) is a good guide to giving them plenty of space and preventing bullying, with one or two other similar size fields available so the grass can be rested.

Note that these suggestions are based on

providing all the necessary grazing, and may also enable some hay to be taken. However, there is always the problem of the unevenness of seasonal growth – too much in spring, not enough in winter. Many horse owners find it easier to adjust to spring and summer growth by having a small amount of land where the quality of the grass is of little interest, and giving additional feed when necessary. With particular emphasis on avoiding obese or laminitic horses this is often seen as the preferred option. However, as explained in previous chapters, if winter grazing is to take place at all, sufficient land must be provided, which will mean managing the spring and summer growth by keeping the excess cut, shutting areas up or taking hay. This is far better for the horse and for the grass, and for your pocket as less feed has to be bought in.

There is also the option of renting extra summer grazing so that smaller areas of permanent grazing, perhaps nearest the stables, can be saved for winter. In many areas of the country there is now excess grass, as numbers of sheep and cattle are diminishing year by year. Farmers and land owners are often on the lookout for grazing animals to help them manage their land, especially semi-natural grassland which they may not be able to manage easily in other ways. Though this presents an excellent opportunity for horse owners, unfortunately horses do not have a good reputation as grazers. The reputation stems from poor management, so if you can show that yours is good and that the animals will be removed often enough to allow the grass to recover, it is an excellent and often economical way of dealing with the land problem.

AVOID PLOUGHING AND RE-ESTABLISHING

If you have a badly degraded pasture with a lot of undesirable weeds, including weed grasses, the temptation is very strong simply to plough it all up and start with a new seed mix: which may well be the advice given by farmers, contractors and other pasture specialists. However, as explained in Chapter 3, this will almost certainly cause more problems than it will solve, and should be avoided if possible.

If the soil is badly compacted and there is a serious infestation of poisonous weeds such as ragwort or bracken, ploughing and re-seeding can be contemplated, but bear in mind that it will take several years before the new pasture can support a full grazing régime. Other options are to spray off all or part of the vegetation, harrow and re-seed or oversow. If soil is compacted, use a subsoiler first.

Remember that the use of chemical sprays needs to be thoroughly considered and carefully planned. Sprays can be damaging to water, wildlife and the health of both humans and horses – and to beneficial vegetation. Before you spray always be sure that you know what plants are present, as you may have pockets of valuable species even in a weedy pasture. If spraying is not an option – either because there is a good range of species or for other reasons – there are alternative ways of renovating a pasture, though they are likely to take longer. One or two seasons of constant cutting to weaken weed species; grazing by sheep and cattle; and shutting up for a hay crop can break the cycle and help to bring the pasture back to better condition.

Re-seeding or overseeding can take place in a number of circumstances other than just starting a new pasture from arable or ploughed land. It can be after the whole field has been sprayed off because of inappropriate vegetation, or if bad patches such as nettle beds have been sprayed or cut, or where serious poaching has taken place. It can also be done to introduce new grass and flower species into an existing pasture (see p. 104). To re-seed into bare or sprayed patches, harrow hard so that there is an even surface of fine soil. Grass seed is very small and does not have to be drilled into the soil or buried, but can simply be broadcast or spread on to a receptive surface.

Grass seed mixtures were discussed in Chapter 3. The most important factor is avoiding the High Sugar ryegrasses; if possible, avoid ryegrass altogether unless you are very sure that it is a native-type variety with low sugar content. Native grasses are the most suitable, but they can be expensive. Wildflowers such as yarrow and bird's-foot trefoil will add to the interest of the grass, both for the horse and for wildlife.

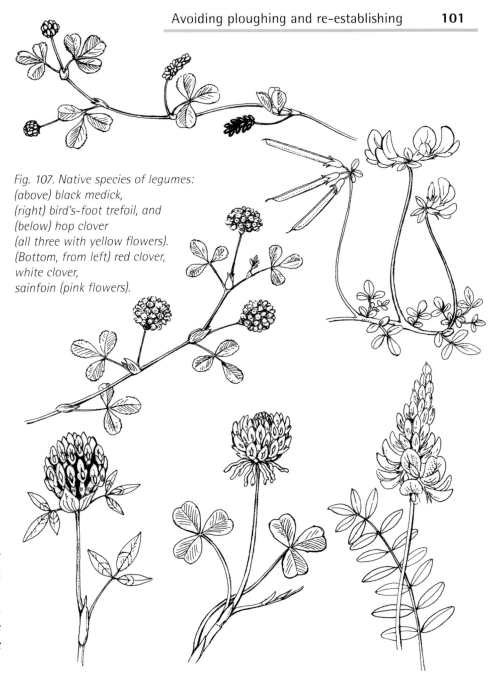

Fig. 107. Native species of legumes: (above) black medick, (right) bird's-foot trefoil, and (below) hop clover (all three with yellow flowers). (Bottom, from left) red clover, white clover, sainfoin (pink flowers).

AVOID ARTIFICIAL NITROGEN FERTILISER

Livestock farmers will often tell you that grass cannot be properly managed without some fertiliser, and there is no doubt that nitrogen boosts production and helps to smother out weeds. Chapters 3 and 4 explained why this kind of management does not suit horses, and how it is quite possible to have good, suitable grassland without the use of artificial fertilisers. Nonetheless, it was also noted that some kind of slow-release fertiliser for the addition of phosphorous, potash and lime might be helpful occasionally. If the soil is poor and the horses are not prone to obesity and laminitis, the introduction of small amounts of native species of red and white clover will help the grass to grow. Other legumes such as bird's-foot trefoil, hop clover, black medick and sainfoin (fig. 107) will also add a little bit of organic nitrogen to the soil.

Spreading well-rotted farmyard or stable manure every few years will help to provide a range of nutrients and add organic matter to the soil.

REST PADDOCKS

The need for grass to have a chance to recover from grazing must be recognised, particularly with horses because of their ability to graze so short and their habit of returning again and again to favourite patches. Resting during the growing season also gives vegetation a chance to re-establish on bare patches, and if some seeding is allowed, desirable plants can be encouraged to spread. As long as at least 70% of the sward is free of bare patches the grass can recover if given a reasonable rest period.

Resting at different times of year will also help the balance of species within the vegetation. For example, if a pasture is always rested when grass growth is at its strongest other species such as clover and wildflowers may struggle to compete (which may be an advantage if you are trying to cut down on white clover). Even the grasses have different growing periods so, by varying the resting time, you give all the different species the best chance of survival.

Resting also allows time for work to be undertaken on the pasture, such as harrowing, spraying or re-seeding bare patches. Topping can take place while the horses are grazing, but for the other operations horses need to be out of the pasture for a few weeks. More major operations such as subsoiling or spreading manure may require an even longer resting period.

Another reason for resting pasture is to cut down on parasites, which is also helped by grazing other stock (*see Chapter 4*). If other stock is grazed it may not be necessary to rest pastures for as long, if at all, as long as the stocking rate is low. Cattle in particular will graze different grasses and will not graze as short as horses, so some recovery is possible even while they are grazing. Make sure that fencing is suitable before introducing cattle or sheep. Horse wire with electric tape or electric rope is a good choice for all three species.

MANAGE LATRINES

Some form of latrine management is necessary on all but the most lightly grazed grassland. It does not necessarily mean picking up droppings, though this may be the preferred management on small areas and overstocked pastures, or in circumstances where parasite control is paramount.

Chapter 3 explained that picking up droppings is not beneficial in all circumstances, and that on large or uneven areas it is often not possible, even with the use of sweepers or vacuum machines. In these cases it is very important to keep latrine areas topped (to avoid weeds spreading to other areas), and harrowed where possible. It may be necessary to rest fields for longer – twelve weeks or more – if droppings cannot be regularly dealt with.

TOP WEEDS AND RANK GROWTH

Keeping grass from heading and seeding will encourage it to produce leaves and be more productive. Regular topping is thus a good way of keeping a sward growing well without the use of fertiliser, and is a practice which should be followed where a productive sward is required. It will also help to reduce the incidence of unwanted weeds such as nettles and thistles. Always remember to check for ragwort, and remove it before topping takes place.

A good approach to topping is to time it when the grass has been grazed to 3 to 5 cm. Any weeds and rank vegetation will then be obvious and the mower can be set above the level of the grazed grass so as not to cut any desirable wildflowers (which are generally small) or to create too much cut material. The horses can be left on the field for a few days longer (during which time they will graze and kick around the cuttings) and then be moved on to fresh pasture. At this time the empty field can be harrowed to spread the rest of the cuttings and any droppings evenly across the field, and left to rest and regrow.

There are some circumstances where regular topping may not be appropriate:

• Where you want a less productive sward, grasses can be allowed to mature. This may be useful where there is too much grass available; horses can be confined to an area small enough for them to graze evenly, and the rest can be shut up until autumn when the seeded grasses will form a high fibre, low sugar forage for winter (but be wary of large amounts of wet grass, which can cause colic or carry mould).
• If you have a lot of wildflowers you will need to top less frequently, or to make sure that the topper is set to avoid their growth points, which are generally higher above the ground than the growth point of grasses.
• If you are trying to encourage certain grasses or flowers to spread, you may want to allow them to seed and not do any topping until late July or August.

AVOID POACHING AND OVERGRAZING

Poaching and overgrazing are probably the two most important management issues in horse grazing, and of course are closely linked to all the points mentioned earlier, as the management discussed so far influences the ability to avoid poaching in wet weather and overgrazing all year round. Chapter 3 covered a number of ways of managing winter grazing so that poaching can be avoided or at least kept to a minimum.

Fig. 108. Grass worn away to bare ground in summer will quickly turn to mud in winter.

Poaching is often the result of overgrazing, which creates bare patches where the soil is unstable (fig. 108) and can be quickly turned to mud. A good dense vegetation cover will help to avoid poaching, but in very wet circumstances even this will not be enough to prevent it.

With regard to overgrazing, remember that allowing a horse to graze very short is not good for either the horse or the sward. If you are using it as a way to keep the horse from putting on weight you are probably upsetting his digestive system by not giving him enough suitable high fibre, low carbohydrate food. You are certainly making problems for yourself in the future by allowing the horse to graze out all the best grasses, leaving room for annual grasses and weeds.

DIVERSIFY THE SWARD

Perhaps this could be described as the 'icing on the cake' of creating the perfect pasture. There are two good reasons for trying to create a flower-filled pasture for your horse: first because the little research we have suggests that it is the best type of pasture for horses; and secondly because flower-filled pastures and meadows used to be found all over the country. It is now estimated that only 3% of them are left: which is the same level of reduction as if you started with a standard dressage arena and ended up with a single stable (fig. 109). Chapter 2 explained why flower-filled pastures are important for other reasons than feeding horses. Additionally, as we saw in Chapter 4, grazing horses on monoculture grasslands – those consisting of mainly ryegrass which are sprayed and fertilised to keep them that way – is like feeding them on junk food, high in sugar and chemical additives and without sufficient minerals, trace elements and fibre. In contrast a species-rich pasture offers a more balanced, non-fattening diet with more of the type of feed from which horses benefit.

It is not always easy to introduce new species into existing grassland, so the first step is to be sure that good management is already in place. If grass is allowed to be overgrazed or poached and latrine areas are not managed, new species are unlikely to establish and survive, so the cost and effort of introducing them would be wasted. Having said that, very short grass with some bare patches is a useful way of introducing new species! There will be areas of soil for them to establish in, and less competition from existing vegetation. But it is not the only method of achieving the desired end.

A good way of ensuring that new grasses and flowers will be able to establish and persist in a field which is already grass is to spray off strips (about half a metre wide) or patches (about a metre square), then prepare the soil and sow the seed (fig. 110). If there is already a good range of grasses in the field, only wildflowers need be sown; they will be able to grow without being overtaken by the older vegetation, and over time they will spread out into the field. This is also a much less expensive approach than trying to seed the whole field, and can be carried out on an experimental basis in small areas to see how successful both the establishment and the subsequent management are before undertaking more ambitious projects.

If your pasture already has a good range of grasses and flowers but you want to increase them or spread them into neighbouring fields, you should use the seed that is already in the pasture rather than introducing an off-the-shelf mix. Even if you buy native seed, grasses and flowers can produce types which are very local and well-suited to their surroundings, and if this is the case you do not want to dilute years of adaptation by introducing types from elsewhere. You can thus take seed from your own pasture – either by cutting hay just as the seed becomes ripe and spreading it thinly on the ground, or by harvesting the seed (fig. 111) and sowing it as described above. Note that if you have a good species-rich pasture you should always take expert advice before undertaking any re-seeding.

Fig. 109. Flower-filled grasslands in England and Wales were once common; since the 1960s, we have lost 97% of them.

Fig. 110. Cowslips growing in straight lines after wildflowers have been re-introduced into grassland by the method of spraying off and re-sowing parallel strips.

Fig. 111. A seed harvester, a specialist machine for collecting local flower and grass seed for sowing.

CONCLUSION

Pasture management can be undertaken on many levels, depending on the amount of land you have and the equipment at your disposal. Your own choices and goals play a large part in the actual management techniques that you apply: for example you may want your grass to be the main source of food for your horse, or you may be mainly looking for turn-out; you may be happy to use chemicals and sprays or you may prefer to use more natural management; you may want to encourage wildlife as well as look after your horse (fig. 112).

Most importantly pasture management should be an integral part of looking after your horses and ponies. It has a vital role to play in their health and well-being, and they are probably happiest when out at grass. Managing your pasture can become a rewarding and fascinating part of horse-keeping, rather than just another chore.

Fig. 112. A varied and healthy sward.

GLOSSARY

Acid Of soils, measuring below a pH of 5; lacking in calcium.

Acre Unit of land measurement (imperial), equal to 4840 square yards or 4046 square metres (0.4 hectares).

Aerator Machine for loosening compacted soil beneath the surface; penetrates to less depth than a subsoiler.

Aftermath The grass which re-grows after hay has been cut; often grazed.

Alkaline Of soils, measuring 7 pH or above; high in calcium.

Annual Of a plant, surviving for one year only and reliant on re-growth from seed.

Awns Slender bristles on parts of the floret of some grasses.

Basic slag Bi-product of the steel industry used as a phosphorus fertiliser.

Bent grass Family of grasses which includes common bent and creeping bent, often found in horse pastures.

Biennial A plant which lives for two years only.

Browser An animal which eats mainly vegetation from the shrub layer, i.e. twigs and shoots, rather than grasses.

Chewings' fescue A type of red fescue, often used in seed mixes for horse pastures because of its ability to form a dense turf; generally liked by horses.

Crude protein A definition of the content of foodstuffs, derived from the percentage of nitrogen (which in food is generally in the form of protein).

Digestible energy The availability to the horse of the energy in foodstuffs, calculated from the difference between the total energy content of the food and the loss of energy into the faeces.

Diploid Having a regular (double) set of chromosones; of ryegrass, both the common varieties and the High Sugar varieties which are low-growing and turf-forming.

Dry matter Food substances with all water content removed.

Encysted redworm Redworm larva which has burrowed into the gut wall and surrounded itself with a cyst or closed capsule.

Enzymes Substances produced in the intestines which help to break down fibre into energy.

Environmental Impact Assessment A set of regulations which assess the impact of changes to land use, such as fertilising or ploughing up species-rich grassland, to help prevent the loss of semi-natural habitat.

Feral An animal living in a wild state but with domesticated ancestors, such as the mustang.

Haylage A method of conserving grass with a higher moisture content than hay but less fermentation than silage, suitable for horses.

Hectare Unit of land measurement (metric), equal to 10,000 square metres, 2.47 acres.

Hyperlipaemia A condition caused (often in obese animals) when food is withdrawn, resulting in excess fat in the bloodstream; symptoms include lack of appetite, depression, weakness and twitching muscles.

Improved grassland Referring to agricultural grass-land which has been drained, re-seeded and kept free of weeds to increase its productivity; usually refers to grass consisting of at least 30% ryegrass.

Joule A unit of energy, work or heat; used as a measurement of digestible energy.

Legume A type of plant which fixes nitrogen from the air by means of a bacteria living in its root nodules; includes members of the pea family such as clover, vetches, trefoils and sainfoin.

Ligule Membranous growth where the leaf of a grass meets the stem.

Megajoule A million joules.

Mole-drainer An agricultural machine which makes drainage channels in the soil by means of a hoe-shaped blade pulling an expander about half a metre below ground.

Organic matter Living things, or the remains of living things; *see soil organic matter.*

Perennial Of a plant, surviving for more than two years.

Proteins The building blocks of all living cells and an essential part of the diet.

Quidding Dropping food from the mouth, usually as a result of problems with teeth.

Ridge and furrow A formation of humps and hollows seen in old grassland, the remnants of medieval agricultural systems; also called rigg and furrow.

Semi-feral Domesticated animals living in a wild state but individually identified and in ownership, such as British native ponies.

Semi-natural grassland Grassland which is grazed or cut for hay but receives no other management and so consists of the plants adapted to the specific soil, climate etc. of the area.

Silica The most abundant mineral on earth, it strengthens plant cells to protect them from being eaten, so requires teeth and a digestive system which can deal with it.

Slitter Machine which creates slits in the sward, helping to improve drainage and root growth.

Soil organic matter In the topsoil, the remains of living things, both animal and vegetable.

Soil organisms The living inhabitants of the soil, including animals (earthworms, nematodes, beetles, mites), fungi and micro-organisms.

Spot spraying, spot treatment The targeted use of herbicides on just the problem plants, as opposed to blanket spraying of the whole sward.

Starch A simple carbohydrate made by plants which is digested into glucose by enzymes to give energy; particularly found in cereal grains such as oats and barley, also in the seed heads of grass.

Stolons Shoots from the base of the plant which creep along the ground to root and produce new stems.

Stocking rate The number of animals carried on a given area of land, usually expressed as live-stock units per hectare; one cow or one horse is equal to one livestock unit (youngstock, ponies and sheep are fractions of a livestock unit).

Subsoiler An agricultural machine consisting of heavy tines dragged at depths of around half a metre to break up compacted soil.

Sward Grassy surface, turf.

Tetraploid Having four sets of chromosones; of ryegrass, taller, less dense varieties than diploid varieties, with higher sugar levels than normal diploid varieties but not as high as High Sugar ryegrasses.

Tilth Cultivated soil or soil-like material.

Tines Spikes of various lengths on agricultural machinery, such as harrows.

Tillers Side shoots (leaves) from the base of a grass stem.

Weed wiper A machine (hand-held or tractor mounted) for applying herbicide to the weeds which stand up above the majority of the vegetation; the herbicide is wiped on to the leaves.

Fig. 113. A pasture of slow growing, hard-wearing native grasses which with careful management stands up well to winter use.

INDEX